Practical Strategies for Electronic Structure Calculations

Warren J. Hehre   Department of Chemistry
University of California
Irvine, California 92717   USA

Wavefunction, Inc.
18401 Von Karman, Suite 370
Irvine, California 92715   USA

Practical Strategies
for Electronic Structure
Calculations

Warren J. Hehre   Department of Chemistry
University of California
Irvine, California 92717   USA

Wavefunction, Inc.
18401 Von Karman, Suite 370
Irvine, California 92715   USA

Wavefunction (Irvine, California, USA)
1995

Printed in the United States of America

ISBN 0-9643495-1-5

Acknowledgments

Many people have contributed to this book. A few deserve special mention. Scientific contributors from among my doctoral students at the University of California at Irvine include Tammy Chao, Richard Dixon, Scott Fielder and Wayne Huang. Alan Shusterman at Reed College has furnished many ideas throughout this project. The scientists and staff at Wavefunction, in particular, Lonnie Burke, Bernard Deppmeier, Andy Diessen, Harry Johnson and Joe Leonard, have contributed their valuable insights to this effort. This manuscript was prepared throughout its many drafts by Carmen Lloyd, Rob Misheloff and Monica Scott. Wayne Huang assisted greatly with the final illustrations. The final text was prepared for printing by Alan Graham and Michael Hendrickson from Words & Pictures Press.

Preface

This book, which has developed out of a short course given at Wavefunction, Inc. over the past three years, is intended to serve as a guide to the use of modern electronic structure calculations, including semi-empirical molecular orbital calculations, Hartree-Fock and correlated molecular orbital calculations and density functional calculations. Its intended audience are research chemists and students of chemistry who wish to apply computational techniques to investigate real chemical problems. Its focus is entirely on the practical aspects of carrying out calculations, covering such topics as the choice of equilibrium and transition-state geometries and the effective use of energies and other quantities resulting from the calculations. Coverage is very brief, with no attempt made to derive or detail the computational methods discussed. Some effort has been expended to assess the performance of the various levels of calculation with respect to certain key quantities, in particular, equilibrium structure and reaction energetics, although for the most part our remarks here are very general. Detailed description of methods and critical and thorough assessment of their performance have been covered in depth elsewhere.[1] We have also not attempted to detail specific chemistry resulting from application of electronic structure methods, for this again, is not our primary purpose.

Most of the examples have been drawn from organic chemistry, although some material relating to molecules incorporating heavier main-group elements has been included. Missing is material for transition metal inorganics and organometallics. Practical and reliable electronic structure methods for

---

1. (a) W.J. Hehre, L. Radom, P.v.R. Schleyer and J.A. Pople, **Ab Initio Molecular Orbital Theory**, Chapter 6, Wiley, New York, 1986; (b) W.J. Hehre, **Critical Assessment of Modern Electronic Structure Methods**, Wavefunction, Inc. Irvine, California, 1995.

transition metal systems are just now beginning to appear, and the author does not yet feel that there is sufficient experience with their use to propose effective strategies.

Each of the chapters, which follows a brief introduction, deals with a single practical aspect encountered when performing calculations: **Obtaining and Using Equilibrium Geometries, Obtaining Transition Structures and Verifying Reaction Pathways, Making Use of Energy Data for Thermochemical Comparisons, Making Use of Energy Data for Kinetic Comparisons, Dealing with Conformationally Flexible Molecules,** and **Obtaining Atomic Charges.** A final chapter, **Graphical Models and Modeling Strategies,** describes and illustrates a number of graphical techniques useful for the description of molecular structure and chemical reactivity.

Each chapter itself comprises a brief introduction followed by a series of questions, ranging from those which are strictly informative, *"Why is finding a transition structure more difficult than finding an equilibrium structure?"*, to those with obviously practical aims, *"Is it always necessary to utilize exact equilibrium geometries in carrying out thermochemical comparisons, or will geometries obtained from lower-level calculations suffice?"*, and all varieties in between. In answering questions, we have drawn on actual computational examples using one or more "standard" electronic structure models. These include, but are not restricted to, the AM1[2] semi-empirical model, Hartree-Fock models with the STO-3G, 3-21G and 6-31G* basis sets[3], the MP2/6-31G* correlated model, and the SVWN/6-31G* and Becke3LYP/6-31G* (B3LYP/6-31G*) density functional models.[4] We believe that the general conclusions which we have drawn regarding both the efficient application and effective use of these particular electronic structure models, as well as any advice to assist in their application, are also applicable to other methods.

The performance of electronic structure methods with regard to the calculation of equilibrium geometries and relative energies is briefly surveyed in **Appendix A**. Rough indication of the relative costs of application of the different models is also provided here. **Appendix B** provides a glossary of terms commonly encountered. **Appendix C** summarizes the "units" used throughout this book.

We have provided a "non-conventional" index to this book. It is in the form of a two-dimensional chart, molecular and chemical properties listed in one dimension and issues concerning these properties in the other. Entries reference questions discussed in text which address the issues for the specific properties of concern.

This book contains a great deal of data, both from experiment and from calculation. It also no doubt contains errors, and these are the sole responsibility of the author. Hopefully, most of the "glaring mistakes" have been caught, and what remains will not significantly alter the conclusions presented.

All semi-empirical and Hartree-Fock molecular orbital calculations and some of the MP2 correlated calculations reported in this book have been carried

---

2. M.J.S. Dewar, E.G. Zoebisch, E.F. Healy and J.J.P. Stewart, J. Am. Chem. Soc., **107**, 3902 (1985).
3. See ref 1A, Chapters 2 and 4.
4. This method mixes the Hartree-Fock exchange with the Becke exchange functional, and uses the correlation functional due to Lee, Yang and Parr. It involves three parameters chosen by fitting experimental heats of formation.

out using *SPARTAN*.[5] The remaining MP2 calculations and all density functional calculations have been carried out using Gaussian 92/DFT[6] as interfaced to *SPARTAN*. While we have attempted to keep our remarks general, i.e., independent of a specific program wherever possible, many of the strategies recommended have been implemented inside of *SPARTAN* and, therefore, are particularly convenient.

5. *SPARTAN* 4.0, Wavefunction, Inc., 18401 Von Karman, Suite 370, Irvine, California 92715.
6. Gaussian 92/DFT, Gaussian, Inc., Carnegie Office Park, Building 6, Pittsburgh, Pennsylvania 15106.

Table of Contents

1

Introduction

Calculations, in particular molecular mechanics calculations and electronic structure calculations, play a multiple role in modern-day chemistry. First they serve to supply information about the structures, relative stabilities and other properties of isolated molecules. In this regard, they serve to supplement and, more and more, replace traditional experimental methods. While electronic structure methods were originally developed to describe the properties of isolated (gas phase) molecules, a number of models are now available which account for solvent. This is a relatively new development, but we can expect to see numerous applications in the near future.

Calculations, in particular electronic structure calculations, are also called on to furnish information about the mechanisms and product distributions of chemical reactions, either directly by examining the structures and relative energies of reaction transition states, or indirectly by modeling the steric and electronic demands of the reactants. Quantitative quantum chemical calculations leading directly to information about transition states and reaction mechanisms are likely to become more common, while qualitative (reactant-based) models will always be needed for systems which are too large to be subjected to the more rigorous treatments. It is the description of chemical reactivity and product selectivity which most clearly distinguishes in an operational sense electronic structure methods from present generation empirical molecular mechanics schemes. The latter tell us nothing either about electronic charge distributions (allowing us to anticipate how a given molecule might react), or about the structures and relative stabilities of transition states.

Finally, electronic structure calculations are now being used routinely in support or in lieu of experiment to supply "parameters" needed as input for other techniques, for example, atomic charges for QSAR analyses. *Ab initio* molecular orbital calculations, in particular, are also able to provide accurate intra- and intermolecular potentials, that is, information linking structure to energy. This information is required both by *molecular mechanics* and by *molecular dynamics* techniques used to describe a wide variety of phenomena, ranging from interactions between an enzyme and a drug to the physical properties of polymeric materials. All of these tasks are too complex to now be treated using quantum mechanical models, even semi-empirical quantum mechanical models. Non-empirical electronic structure methods can also be the best source of data for parameterizing next-generation semi-empirical molecular orbital models to account not only for the (known) structures and properties of equilibrium species but also for those corresponding to transition states, extending their range of application.

The future appears to be very bright. Major advances in hardware and software technologies over the past decade have now made sophisticated quantum mechanical calculations applicable to systems of real chemical interest, and affordable and accessible to chemists. Quantum chemical models will no doubt continue to displace empirical mechanics based schemes in more and more areas, while the simpler models will likely be applied to systems of ever increasing size and complexity. More importantly, the role of computational methods in general as a legitimate means of doing chemistry will continue to expand.

The missing component in the application of computation to chemistry, as in the evolution of any new approach, is an understanding of exactly how this technology can be applied. In other words, for what kinds of problems are computational methods appropriate, what kinds of answers are to be expected, and most practically, how exactly are computational investigations to be carried out. All of these questions can only be answered by numerous and varied examples, ranging from examples intended to teach fundamental chemical principles, to "laboratory exercises" intended to develop and refine skills in the use of computational methods, to actual research problems where computation supplements or even replaces experiment. There is now enough experience with several different classes of methods, and with a number of specific models in particular, to allow some answers to these kinds of questions and some generalizations to be made. Providing these answers and establishing broad generalizations are the primary goals of this book.

Electronic structure methods may be divided into four distinct classes: *ab initio* Hartree-Fock methods, *ab initio* correlated methods, density functional methods and semi-empirical methods. Within each class, many variations may occur, for example, variations in basis set, method and level of inclusion of electron correlation for *ab initio* methods, choice of functionals as well as basis set for density functional methods, and for semi-empirical models, details of parameterization. A summary of the "practical range" of application of each of the classes of methods, together with indication of the present level of experience is provided in **Table 1-1**. Needless to say, our observations are subjective.

Both *ab initio* Hartree-Fock and semi-empirical molecular orbital models have been in widespread use for many years, and there is now a great deal of experience in their application. While the majority of this experience is for calculations involving light main-group elements (applications to organic chemistry), a significant number of applications involving heavier main-group

Table 1-1: Range of Application and Experience of Electronic Structure Methods

electronic structure method	available elements	molecular size (atoms)	experience
ab initio Hartree-Fock	1st half of Periodic Table	50	extensive
ab initio correlated	light main group	20	limited
density functional	1st half of Periodic Table	50	very limited
semi-empirical	light main group	200	extensive

elements and very recently transition metals have now been reported. Because of their considerable computational cost, correlated methods are not as thoroughly documented, and their applications have for the most part been restricted to molecules containing light main-group elements. However, some of the lower-level correlated methods, the MP2 method in particular, are rapidly becoming common and have for some applications nearly replaced Hartree-Fock models. Practical applications of density functional methods are only very recent, and it is fair to say that "standards", both insofar as choice of functionals and basis sets, remain to be established.

An overview of the performance of each of the four classes of electronic structure methods is provided in **Table 1-2**. Singled out for consideration are equilibrium and transition state geometries, conformational energy differences and relative thermochemical stabilities. We have also commented on the use of each of the classes of methods as a basis for graphical models. Our classifications are qualitative at best (to some extent they reflect the author's bias), and are not intended to act as critical commentary. (A brief overview of performance is provided in **Appendix A**, and detailed assessment is available elsewhere[1].) Rather, we intend only to provide a rough guide to assist in formulation of overall computational strategies.

All methods successfully account for equilibrium geometries and, with the exception of density functional models where there is not yet enough experience to establish performance and semi-empirical models which sometimes lead to unrealistic results, also appear to properly account for transition-state geometries. Hartree-Fock, correlated and density functional methods also provide reasonable descriptions of conformational energy differences, although many further examples are required to provide an overall level of confidence. Semi-empirical methods are often quite unsatisfactory in describing conformational energy differences, and are also unable to properly and reliably account for relative thermochemical stabilities. The latter are generally well handled by all other classes of electronic structure methods. Only for Hartree-Fock and semi-empirical models is there sufficient experience to comment on use of electronic structure methods for graphical modeling. While the former appear to be suitable, semi-empirical methods have proven to be unreliable for this purpose.

A number of practical strategies follow from these rough classifications. The most important of these follows from the observation that all models generally provide favorable descriptions of equilibrium geometry. Thus, it is reasonable to suggest the use of low-level electronic structure methods (semi-empirical models and small basis set Hartree-Fock models in particular) for equilibrium and transition-state geometry calculations, and only then to call on higher-level methods for energy and property evaluation and for graphics presentation. The primary purpose of this book is to set down and document strategies for efficiently performing and correctly interpreting electronic structure calculations. In so doing, we will attempt to quantify the qualitative interpretations provided in **Table 1-2**.

While this book does not directly concern the use of molecular mechanics methods based on parameterized force fields (except for searching

---

1. W.J. Hehre, L. Radom, P.v.R. Schleyer and J.A. Pople, **Ab Initio Molecular Orbital Theory**, Chapter 6, Wiley, New York, 1986; (b) W.J. Hehre, **Critical Assessment of Modern Electronic Structure Methods**, Wavefunction, Inc., Irvine, California, 1995.

Table 1-2: Performance of Electronic Structure Methods[a]

electronic structure method	equilibrium geometry	transition state geometry	conformational energy differences	thermo-chemistry	basis for graphical models
ab initio Hartree-Fock	G	G	G	G	G
ab initio correlated	G	G	G	G	?
density functional	G	?	G	G	?
semi-empirical	G	M,U	P→M	P	U

a) G = good, M = moderate, P = poor, U = unreliable, ? = unknown.

conformation space where some commentary is provided), it is useful at this stage to point out the essential differences between this class of methods and electronic structure techniques which concern us here. Our remarks are not intended as praise or criticism of either.

Aside from an obvious difference in "cost" of application (molecular mechanics techniques generally increase in cost as the square of the size of the system, while semi-empirical molecular orbital methods increase as the cube of the size and Hartree-Fock models increase as the fourth power of the size), and not commenting at all on the quality of results, there are two major differences:

i) Electronic structure methods, unlike molecular mechanics methods, are not restricted to the description of equilibrium geometry. They are able to provide information both about non-equilibrium structures, for example, transition stuctures as well as overall reaction pathways, and about the electronic structures (charge distributions) of molecules. Both of these are essential to extend application of computation into problems dealing with chemical reactivity and product selectivity.

ii) *Ab initio* electronic structure methods make no explicit use of experimental information. What this means is that a level of confidence, once established by comparison with experimental results, should carry over to areas where no experimental results are available. On the other hand, molecular mechanics schemes are explicitly parameterized to reproduce known experimental results, and should perform best for systems very close to those on which the original parameterization was based. They are likely to lead to uncertain results for systems which are far removed.

Semi-empirical electronic structure methods and some density functional methods represent intermediate situations, in that they incorporate the "basic physics", but also make use of a limited number of parameters. We would expect intermediate behavior.

2

Obtaining and Using
Equilibrium Geometries

The energy of a molecule depends on its geometry. Even small changes in structure can lead to quite large changes in total energy. Proper choice of molecular equilibrium geometry is therefore quite important in carrying out computational studies. What geometry should we use? Experimental structures would seem to be the best choice, given that they are available and are accurate. The trouble is, of course, that accurate experimental structures are often not available. Accurate gas-phase structure determinations using such techniques as microwave spectroscopy are very tedious and have generally been restricted to very small molecules. X-ray determinations on solid samples, while evermore routine, often do not provide full geometrical information, and even when they do one must be concerned about the role of the crystalline environment in altering geometry and particularly conformation. Ions present special problems, in that different counterions lead to different geometries, sometimes significantly so. Finally, only a few experimental structures exist for reactive "short-lived" molecules, let alone for molecular complexes including hydrogen-bonded complexes. There is also a practical concern. Locating and inputing into computational techniques complete experimental geometries is often quite tedious to the extent that it might very well prove a significant barrier to applications. All in all, use of experimental geometries in computational studies is not usually a viable alternative.

Another approach might be to employ *idealized* or otherwise *standard* geometries. This should be reasonable given the very high degree of systematics exhibited by a large range of structures, in particular, structures of organic molecules. As mentioned above, however, energies and other properties may be very sensitive to subtle changes in geometry. For example, the main reason that the dipole moment of trimethylamine is significantly smaller than the dipole moment in ammonia is the change in the local geometry about nitrogen. To lessen steric interactions, the CNC bond angle in trimethylamine is significantly larger than the HNH bond angle in ammonia, and the nitrogen lone pair therefore signifcantly less directed. (In the limit of a "planar" nitrogen center, the dipole moment is zero.) Were both ammonia and trimethylamine constrained to incorporate a tetrahedral nitrogen, then the relative magnitudes of the two dipole moments might not be properly reproduced. Another problem with the use of standard geometries is that the structures of many of the most interesting molecules differ greatly from the norm. All in all, assumed or standard geometries also do not offer a good solution.

In the final analysis, we usually have little choice but to obtain geometries directly from calculation. This is not as difficult a chore as it might appear, at least if we have a reasonable idea where to start. It is also a chore which can be fully automated, and therefore requires no more human effort than a calculation utilizing an experimental or standard geometry. Structure optimization is, however, costly computationally and there are a number of issues associated both with the optimization and use of geometry which need to be raised. These are subjects of the present chapter.

We start with a number of purely practical issues related to strategies for obtaining geometries, including use of low-level methods to provide guesses (**Section 2.1**), verifying that we have attained a local minimum (**Section 2.2**) and the choice of coordinate system (**Section 2.3**). Following this, we address issues regarding choice of basis set (for *ab initio* models), in particular the need for inclusion of (formally) vacant p-functions on alkali and alkaline-earth elements (**Section 2.4**) and vacant d-functions on heavy main-group elements (**Section 2.5**). The effect of electron correlation on equilibrium structure is discussed in **Section 2.6**, and closely associated with this, the importance of d functions for geometry descriptions using correlated (including density functional) models (**Section 2.7**). **Section 2.8** raises the important question of whether or not "practical methods" accounting explicitly for electron correlation always provide better descriptions of molecular equilibrium geometry than Hartree-Fock models. The next four sections explore the use of "approximate" equilibrium structures for thermochemical and property comparisons. **Section 2.9** addresses the issue of whether semi-empirical and low-level *ab initio* models provide geometries which are sufficiently close to geometries obtained from higher-level Hartree-Fock and correlated treatments to be suitable for thermochemical comparisons, and **Section 2.10** asks whether geometries for anions obtained from basis sets incorporating diffuse functions are required for thermochemical comparisons. **Sections 2.11** and **2.12** look for cases in which use of approximate geometries are likely to lead to unsatisfactory or completely meaningless results. The chapter concludes (**Section 2.13**) with a brief discussion of whether equilibrium structure changes significantly in going from the gas phase into solution. Can we compare experimental geometries for liquids obtained in solution with "gas phase" computational results? Can gas phase structures be used for solvent calculations?

2.1 What is the most efficient way to obtain equilibrium geometries?

It is well established that semi-empirical and low-level Hartree-Fock models generally (but not always) provide a reasonable account of molecular equilibrium geometries.[1] Consider for example the performance of the semi-empirical AM1 model and Hartree-Fock models with STO-3G and 3-21G[*] basis sets in reproducing bond distances connecting heavy atoms in two-heavy-atom hydrides comprising first and second-row elements (**Table 2-1** and **Figures 2-1 to 2-3**). All methods perform reasonably well, 3-21G[*] the best of the three and AM1 the worst. The only large bond-length errors at the HF/3-21G[*] level are for compounds of lithium and sodium. The STO-3G model also performs poorly here, as it does for compounds involving two highly electronegative elements, e.g., F_2. Significant errors (0.04-0.06 Å) are common at the AM1 level.

Additional comparisons of bond lengths connecting heavy atoms in hypervalent compounds are provided in **Table 2-2** and **Figures 2-4 to 2-6** (for AM1, STO-3G and 3-21G[*] models, respectively). Both AM1 and STO-3G perform very poorly, and cannot be recommended. On the other hand, the HF/3-21G[*] method performs very well (comparable to its performance for bond lengths in normal valent compounds).

In general, semi-empirical models may present difficulties for classes of molecules for which they have not been explicitly parameterized, e.g., charged species and radicals, but situations where calculated structures are outlandish are actually quite rare. When in doubt, calculations on model systems for which experimental structure data are well known should be performed.

Low-level models (including semi-empirical models) are also generally successful in accounting for the vibrational spectra of stable molecules, at least in a qualitative sense.[1] As such, they can usually be called on to provide a guess at the matrix of second energy derivatives (the Hessian). Again, there will be exceptions to this generalization (especially for semi-empirical methods), and calculations on model systems may be necessary to establish an overall level of confidence.

Once their performance has been established, it is nearly always advantageous to utilize low-level models to provide a guess at either equilibrium geometry or Hessian or both. Some typical results of the kinds of savings that might be expected are displayed in **Table 2-3**. Here the "low level" model is AM1 and the "high level" model is 3-21G. The reference (null) point is molecular mechanics using the SYBYL force field.[2] We do not wish to imply that SYBYL (or molecular mechanics in general) is particularly bad for structure calculation, or that AM1 is particularly good. Some mechanics schemes (in particular newer methods like MM3[3]) often provide better geometries than semi-empirical methods. Rather, we wish only to point out the effect of starting geometry and Hessian, on the rate of convergence.

Except for norbornane, the examples provided all show significant reduction in the number of cycles required for optimization following the use of AM1 geometries and/or AM1 Hessian. Comparisons involving other

1. (a) W.J. Hehre, L. Radom, P.v.R. Schleyer and J.A. Pople, **Ab Initio Molecular Orbital Theory**, Chapter 6, Wiley, New York, 1986; (b) W.J. Hehre, **Critical Assessment of Modern Electronic Structure Methods**, Wavefunction, Inc., Irvine, California, 1995.
2. M.Clark, R.D. Cramer III and N. van Opdensch, J. Computational Chem., **10**, 982 (1989).
3. Review: J.P. Bowen and N.L. Allinger, Revs. in Computational Chem., **2**, 81 (1991).

Table 2-1: Central Bond Lengths in Two Heavy Atom Hydrides

	AM1	STO-3G	3-21G$^{(*)}$	expt.
Li$_2$	—	2.698	2.816	2.673
LiOH	—	1.432	1.537	1.582
LiF	—	1.407	1.520	1.564
LiCl	—	1.933	2.091	2.021
B$_2$H$_6$	1.752	1.805	1.786	1.763
C$_2$H$_2$	1.195	1.168	1.188	1.203
C$_2$H$_4$	1.326	1.306	1.315	1.339
C$_2$H$_6$	1.500	1.538	1.542	1.531
HCN	1.160	1.153	1.137	1.153
HNC	1.178	1.170	1.160	1.169
CH$_2$NH	1.270	1.273	1.256	1.273
CH$_3$NH$_2$	1.432	1.486	1.471	1.471
CO	1.171	1.146	1.129	1.128
H$_2$CO	1.227	1.217	1.207	1.208
CH$_3$OH	1.411	1.433	1.441	1.421
CH$_3$F	1.375	1.384	1.404	1.383
CH$_3$SiH$_3$	1.807	1.861	1.883	1.867
HCP	1.410	1.472	1.513	1.540
CH$_2$PH	1.536	1.615	1.652	1.67
CH$_3$PH$_2$	1.726	1.841	1.855	1.862
CS	1.429	1.519	1.522	1.535
H$_2$CS	1.512	1.574	1.594	1.611
CH$_3$SH	1.754	1.798	1.823	1.819
CH$_3$Cl	1.741	1.802	1.806	1.781
N$_2$	1.106	1.134	1.083	1.098
N$_2$H$_2$	1.212	1.267	1.239	1.252
N$_2$H$_4$	1.378	1.459	1.451	1.449
HNO	1.157	1.231	1.217	1.212
NH$_2$OH	1.324	1.420	1.472	1.453
NP	1.382	1.459	1.462	1.491
H$_2$O$_2$	1.300	1.396	1.473	1.452
HOF	1.367	1.355	1.439	1.442
NaOH	—	1.763	1.865	1.95
MgO	—	1.706	1.731	1.749
SiO	1.571	1.475	1.496	1.510

Table 2-1: Central Bond Lengths in Two Heavy Atom Hydrides (continued)

	AM1	STO-3G	3-21G$^{(*)}$	expt.
HPO	1.461	1.515	1.471	1.512
HOCl	1.733	1.737	1.700	1.690
F_2	1.427	1.315	1.402	1.412
NaF	—	1.753	1.831	1.926
SiH_3F	1.621	1.624	1.593	1.596
ClF	1.647	1.677	1.636	1.628
Na_2	—	2.359	2.651	3.078
NaCl	—	2.221	2.392	2.361
Si_2H_6	2.417	2.243	2.342	2.327
SiH_3Cl	2.071	2.089	2.056	2.048
P_2	1.623	1.808	1.853	1.893
P_2H_4	1.990	2.175	2.205	2.219
H_2S_2	2.107	2.065	2.057	2.055
Cl_2	1.918	2.063	1.996	1.988

Figure 2-1: Comparison of Calculated and Experimental Bond Distances in Two-Heavy-Atom Hydrides: AM1 Model

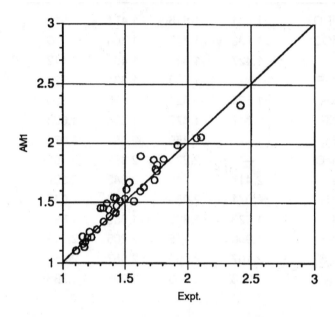

Figure 2-2: Comparison of Calculated and Experimental Bond Distances in Two-Heavy-Atom Hydrides: HF/STO-3G Model

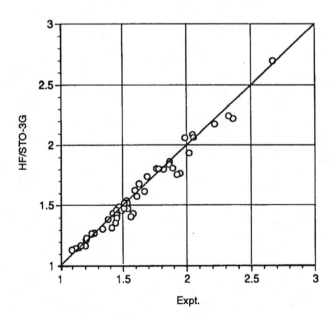

Figure 2-3: Comparison of Calculated and Experimental Bond Distances in Two-Heavy-Atom Hydrides: HF/3-21G(*) Model

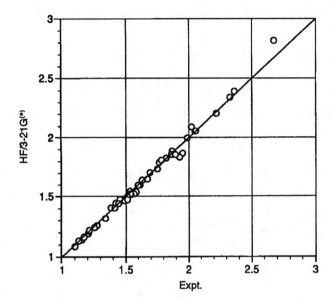

Table 2-2: Structures of Hypervalent Molecules

molecule	bond	AM1	STO-3G	3-21G$^{(*)}$	expt.
PF_5	PF_{eq}	1.535	1.612	1.538	1.534
	PF_{ax}	1.549	1.623	1.566	1.577
$(CH_3)_3PO$	PO	1.462	1.620	1.478	1.479
	PC	1.649	1.840	1.805	1.813
F_3PO	PO	1.451	1.555	1.427	1.436
	PF	1.526	1.606	1.527	1.524
F_3PS	PS	1.874	1.980	1.855	1.866
	PF	1.530	1.615	1.537	1.538
SO_2	SO	1.429	1.675	1.419	1.431
$(CH_3)_2SO$	SO	1.491	1.819	1.490	1.485
	SC	1.739	1.809	1.791	1.799
SF_4	SF_{eq}	1.545	1.675^b	1.550	1.545
	SF_{ax}	1.573	1.675	1.617	1.646
F_2SO	SO	1.434	1.660	1.414	1.413
	SF	1.548	1.650	1.569	1.585
NSF	SN	1.366	1.821	1.440	1.448
	SF	1.581	1.649	1.609	1.643
SO_3	SO	1.351	1.599	1.411	1.420
$(CH_3)_2SO_2$	SO	1.399	1.851	1.438	1.431
	SC	1.690	1.814	1.756	1.777
SF_6	SF	1.540	1.652	1.550	1.564

Table 2-2: **Structures of Hypervalent Molecule s (continued)**

molecule	bond	AM1	STO-3G	3-21G$^{(*)}$	expt.
F_4SO	SO	1.368	1.844[b]	1.413	1.403
	SF_{eq}	1.530	1.671	1.533	1.552
	SF_{ax}	1.549	1.671	1.578	1.575
ClF_3	ClF_{ax}	1.683[a]	1.777	1.676	1.698
	ClF_{eq}	1.683	1.795	1.601	1.598
ClF_5	ClF_{eq}	1.679	1.866	1.599	1.571
	ClF_{ax}	1.694	1.777	1.624	1.669
	ClO	1.675	2.307	1.430	1.418
$FClO_2$	ClF	1.690	1.682	1.618	1.696
	ClO	1.788	2.358	1.408	1.404
$FClO_3$	ClF	1.681	1.683	1.574	1.619

a) Incorrect D_{3h} symmetry structure.

b) Incorrect C_{4v} symmetry structure.

Figure 2-4: Comparison of Calculated and Experimental Bond Distances in Hypervalent Molecules: AM1 Model

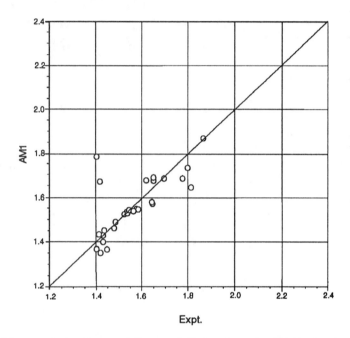

Figure 2-5: Comparison of Calculated and Experimental Bond Distances in Hypervalent Molecules: HF/STO-3G Model

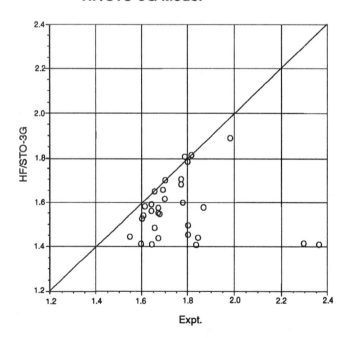

**Figure 2-6: Comparison of Calculated and Experimental
Bond Distances in Hypervalent Molecules:
3-21G$^{(*)}$ Model**

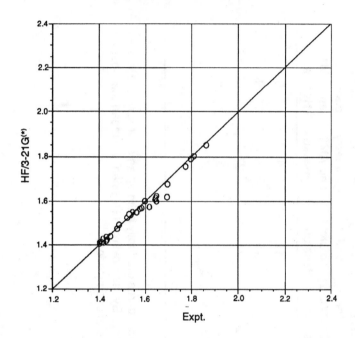

Table 2-3: Number of Cycles Required for Full Geometry Optimization at the HF/3-21G Level as a Function of Starting Geometry and Hessian[a]

molecule	SYBYL geometry and SYBYL Hessian	AM1 geometry and approximate Hessian[b]	SYBYL geometry and AM1 Hessian	AM1 geometry and AM1 Hessian
methylcyclopropyl ether	14	11	9	9
glycine	24	15	21	9
histidine	32	23	27	18
norbornane	6	7	6	5

a) Obtained using SPARTAN.
b) Most geometry optimization procedures gradually build up an approximate Hessian during the course of optimization. By "approximate Hessian" we mean the Hessian which results during the course of optimization.

Hartree-Fock, correlated or density functional methods exhibit similar behavior, as do those where low-level Hartree-Fock models replace semi-empirical methods to provide a guess geometry and Hessian. Given the low relative cost of semi-empirical schemes (full geometry optimization and Hessian calculation usually requiring less time than one optimization cycle of an *ab initio* calculation), it is evident that it is almost always advantageous to make use of them for this purpose.[4]

The case of norbornane warrants individual comment. This molecule is typical of rigid ring systems, and demonstrates the effectiveness of Cartesian optimization procedures (see also **Section 2.3**). The number of required cycles for such types of molecules is usually so small that slightly improved guesses at the geometry and/or Hessian have little or no effect.

One final comment: An excellent guess at an equilibrium geometry is usually provided by the geometry of a closely-related molecule obtained at the same level of calculation. For example, an excellent guess for methylcyclohexane would be cyclohexane.[5] In this case, following modification of the existing geometry, it is usually advantageous to obtain an approximate starting Hessian based on a semi-empirical method. We return to this theme in **Sections 3.4** and **3.7** in discussion of efficient ways to obtain transition states.

2.2 How can we be certain that an "optimized geometry" actually corresponds to a local minimum?

Geometry optimization is an iterative process. The energy and its first derivative with respect to all geometrical coordinates are calculated for the guess geometry, and this information is then used to project a new geometry. This process needs to continue until the lowest energy or *optimized* geometry is reached. Several criteria must be satisfied before a geometry is accepted as optimized. First, successive geometry changes must not lower the total energy by more than a specified (small) value. Second, the energy gradient (first derivative of the energy with respect to geometrical distortions) at the optimized geometry must closely approach zero. This tells us that we are on a *flat* region of the energy surface. Third, successive iterations must not change any geometrical parameter by more than a specified (small) value.

Geometry optimization does not guarantee that the final structure has a lower energy than any other structure of the same molecular formula. All that it guarantees is a *local minimum*, that is, a geometry the energy of which is lower than that of any similar geometry, but which may still not be the lowest energy geometry possible for the molecule. Chemists usually distinguish between sets of local minima which are interconnected by (low energy) rotations about single bonds (**conformers**), and sets of local minima, interconversion among which requires significant bond reorganization (**isomers**). In either case, finding the absolute or *global minimum* requires repeated op-

---

4.   *SPARTAN* facilitates such a strategy by allowing geometry optimization at one level of theory to be preceded by optimization and/or Hessian calculation at a lower level. Thus there is no additional "human time" required to take advantage of potential savings in computer time.

5.   *SPARTAN* facilitates such a tactic by allowing geometry optimization inside the molecule builders subject to some atoms being "frozen". In the case of methylcyclohexane, the underlying ring would be frozen and only the geometry of the methyl group optimized.

timization starting with different initial geometries. The problem of searching conformational space to find the lowest energy or global minimum is discussed in **Section 6.2.**

In principle, structure optimization carried out in the absence of symmetry, i.e., in C_1 symmetry, **must result** in a local minimum. On the other hand, imposition of symmetry may result in a geometry which is not a local minimum. For example, optimization of ammonia constrained to a planar trigonal geometry (D_{3h} symmetry) will result in a structure which corresponds to an energy maximum in the direction of motion toward a puckered trigonal geometry (C_{3v} symmetry). (Indeed, transition states can sometimes be located simply by geometry optimization subject to an overall symmetry constraint.) The most conservative tactic is always to optimize geometry in the absence of symmetry. If this is not practical, one can always verify that the structure located indeed corresponds to a local minimum by performing a normal-mode analysis on the final (optimized) structure. This should yield all real frequencies.[6]

2.3 What coordinate system is most suitable for optimization of equilibrium geometry?

Historically, geometry optimization using quantum mechanical methods has been via internal coordinates (usually in the form of "Z-matrices"),[7] while geometry optimization with empirical molecular mechanics techniques has relied almost exclusively on Cartesian coordinates. At first glance, optimization using internal coordinates might seem to be more efficient than optimization using Cartesian coordinates, and therefore be the method of choice where the energy function is "expensive", while Cartesian coordinates are certainly easier to deal with (from the standpoint of computer graphics), and would provide the better alternative in dealing with "cheap" energy functions. There are advantages and disadvantages to both alternative descriptions, but they are not exactly what first impressions might convey. Internal coordinates (bond lengths, angles and dihedral angles) are obviously familiar to chemists. They are readily transferable from molecule to molecule, and easily lend themselves to optimizations in which one or more distances or angles are fixed. Except for simple molecules, however, internal coordinate representations are difficult to construct. Ring systems in particular present special problems, and one usually needs to resort to such techniques as defining "dummy atoms" (place markers) to deal with them. While automated techniques for constructing internal coordinates from Cartesian coordinates are available, none are unique and more importantly, none lead to representations which are especially efficient for geometry optimization.

On the other hand, Cartesian coordinates are the "natural output" of graphics-based molecule builders, and as such are readily and immediately

---

6.   A normal-normal-mode analysis entails first calculating the complete matrix of second derivatives (the Hessian) for a structure, and then finding the set of coordinates (normal coordinates) which reduces this matrix to diagonal form. The elements of the (diagonal) Hessian are the force constants associated with the normal coordinates; positive force constants correspond to minima and negative force constants to maxima. Vibrational frequencies are related to square root of the force constants (together with mass contributions). Positive force constants lead to real frequencies and negative force constants to imaginary frequencies.

7.   For a discussion see: ref 1a, Chapter 3.

available even for the most complicated molecules. While Cartesian coordinates are certainly not as familiar to chemists as bond lengths and angles, they convert uniquely and, with the aid of computer graphics, automatically into internal coordinates. Finally, techniques have been developed and are available to introduce arbitrary constraints (on bond lengths, angles and dihedral angles) into optimization procedures using Cartesian coordinates.[8] In practice these are actually quite efficient.

Actually the issue is moot. Except for the simplest molecules, internal coordinates (Z matrices) are just too difficult to construct. Even for the very simple systems it will get harder and harder to find chemists who are willing to spend the significant time and effort merely to provide input, when the job can be done in seconds from graphics-based molecule builders.

The only question which remains is how efficient is geometry optimization using Cartesian coordinates, relative to what is generally perceived to be efficient optimization using internal coordinates. This is an important question in view of the large computational cost associated with structure determination using quantum mechanical methods (in contrast to the small cost for molecular mechanics methods where as previously mentioned Cartesian coordinates are well established).

Actually, geometry optimization using Cartesian coordinates appears to be just as efficient as optimization using well-chosen internal coordinates, assuming in both cases that a reasonable Hessian (matrix of second energy derivatives with respect to pairs of coordinates) has been provided.[9] Indeed, Cartesian optimization is generally superior computationally to internal coordinate optimization for cyclic molecules, or for situations in which one or more constraints have been introduced (see also **Section 2.1**). The worst cases for Cartesian optimization are acyclic systems, although even here the differences between the two techniques are usually insignificant.

Cartesian optimization is the way to go! Future efforts should be (and will be) directed at improving them where they are now least effective, rather than in trying to revive internal coordinate optimization methods.

2.4 Are p functions required for accurate Hartree-Fock geometry determinations on molecules incorporating alkali and alkaline-earth elements?

The valence descriptions of alkali and alkaline-earth atoms in their electronic ground states include only s-type functions, e.g., 2s in the case of lithium. However, the common belief is that these elements act not only as strong σ-electron donors in bonding to electronegative elements, but also as π-electron acceptors, e.g., in lithium fluoride.

8. J. Baker, J. Computational Chem., **13**, 240 (1992).
9. J. Baker and W.J. Hehre, J. Computational Chem., **12**, 606 (1991).

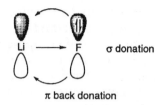

σ donation

π back donation

To the extent that such a picture is correct, it suggests that it will be necessary to include valence p-type functions in the basis set of alkali and alkaline-earth elements, even though these are formally unoccupied (in the ground state atom). Failure to do so should lead to bonding which is weaker (and more ionic) than observed, as would be evidenced by bond lengths which are too long and electric dipole moments which are too large.

Essentially all basis sets now in widespread use provide valence p functions on alkali and alkaline-earth elements. We shall see in the next section that for some compounds even this does not appear to provide adequate description of equilibrium geometries and electric dipole moments. In particular, where chlorine, bromine and iodine are involved, bond distances calculated at the HF/3-21G level are significantly longer than experimental values and dipole moments are significantly larger. Here, d functions need to be added to the halogens (even though these are not occupied in the atomic ground states) to achieve results in much better accord with experiment (see also, **Section 2.1**).

2.5 Are d functions required for accurate Hartree-Fock geometry determinations on molecules incorporating heavy main-group elements?

Hartree-Fock models using the 3-21G split-valence basis set have proven to be remarkably successful in accounting for the equilibrium structures of diverse molecules incorporating hydrogen and first-row elements only.[1] Indeed, it often provides geometries which are superior to those obtained using much larger basis sets which involve a greater degree of valence splitting or include one or more sets of polarization functions.[10] While there are problem situations, e.g., proper description of the local geometry about nitrogen in amines (see **Section 2.12**), these are remarkably few, and the HF/3-21G model is a powerful and practical tool for structure determination.

To what extent does this success carry over to molecules incorporating heavier main-group elements? Are functions of higher angular quantum number than are formally occupied in the atom in its ground state important, or not important as is apparently the case for molecules incorporating first-row elements? These questions are reminiscent of the issues raised in **Section 2-4** regarding the importance of valence p-type functions on the geometries of alkali and alkaline-earth compounds. Here it was suggested that basis sets without valence p functions would lead to structures which were too ionic (bond lengths too long and electric dipole moments too large).

The data in **Tables 2-4** and **2-5** provide a clear answer, at least for Hartree-Fock methods. Here, bond lengths between non-hydrogen atoms (and

---

10. This is fortuitous and is possible because (limiting) Hartree-Fock geometries are not identical to experimental geometries. See also **Section 2.6**.

involving at least one second-row or heavier main-group element) obtained from both 3-21G (unsupplemented) and 3-21G$^{(*)}$ (supplemented by a set of d-type functions) split-valence basis sets are compared with experimental values. Results obtained using the 6-31G* basis set (with d functions on all non-hydrogen atoms) are also provided where available (second-row elements only). Even for normal-valent compounds, i.e., which satisfy the octet rule (**Table 2-4**), are the results dramatic. Without supplementary d-type functions bond-length errors approaching 0.1Å are common, while calculations using the supplemented basis sets (as well as the 6-31G* basis set) yield equilibrium geometries which are generally very close to experimental structures. The situation is not unexpectedly even more dramatic in dealing with hypervalent compounds which do not satisfy the octet rule (**Table 2-5**). Without d functions, bonds to the heavy element are consistently too long, sometimes by 0.2Å and more. A graphical summary of the geometry data presented in **Tables 2-4** and **2-5** is provided in **Figure 2-7**.

Calculated electric dipole moments for a variety of both normal-valent and hypervalent compounds (**Table 2-6**) confirm the belief that inclusion of d-type functions in the basis set is needed to allow back bonding to occur (just as inclusion of p-type functions in alkali and alkaline earth elements did; see **Section 2.4**), and lead to a reduction in overall polarity. As with structure, 3-21G$^{(*)}$ and 6-31G* results are very similar. A graphical summary is provided in **Figure 2-8**. d-functions also improve to some extent the agreement between calculated and measured bond distances and electric dipole moments in alkali and alkaline earth compounds (**Table 2-7**), although there are still large residual errors in some cases.

The overall recommendation is clear. Structure calculations on molecules containing second-row and heavier main-group elements require the use of basis sets which incorporate d-type functions on the heavy atoms. The 3-21G$^{(*)}$ basis set (which does not include d-type functions on first-row elements) is satisfactory, and closely reproduces results obtained from use of the 6-31G* basis set (which also includes d-type functions on first-row elements).

The findings here also carry over for calculations using correlated methods, including density functional methods.[11] In fact, as we shall see in **Section 2.7**, in this case basis sets which include d-type functions are absolutely essential for proper description of equilibrium geometry, even for molecules incorporating only light elements.

2.6 How does electron correlation affect equilibrium geometries calculated at the Hartree-Fock level?

We answer this question qualitatively here and then go on in the next section to provide further details.

---

11. Thiel has developed a semi-empirical method, called MNDO/d, which adds d-type functions to the valence descriptions of heavy main-group elements. Results for the few elements which have been published are significantly better than those obtained from the MNDO model on which MNDO/d is based. (a) W. Thiel and A. Voityuk, Theor. Chim. Acta., **81**, 391 (1992); (b) W. Thiel and A. Voityuk, Int.J. Quantum Chem., **44**, 807, 1992. Note, however, that MNDO/d and PM3 (which does not involve supplementary d functions) lead to comparable (structural) results for heavy main-group elements, leading one to ask whether the improvement of MNDO/d over MNDO is due to the added d functions or simply to improved parameterization.

Table 2-4: **Effect of d Functions on Bond Distances in Molecules Incorporating Second-Row and Heavier Main-Group Elements**

bond	molecule	3-21G	3-21G[*]	6-31G*	expt.
CSi	vinylsilane	1.897	1.867	1.873	1.853
	tetramethylsilane	1.919	1.889	1.894	1.875
CP	trimethylphosphine	1.903	1.848	1.853	1.841
CS	thiophene	1.797	1.722	1.726	1.714
	dimethyl sulfide	1.885	1.813	1.809	1.802
	thiirane	1.934	1.817	1.811	1.815
	methane thiol	1.895	1.823	1.817	1.819
CCl	chloroform	1.835	1.776	1.762	1.758
	carbon tetrachloride	1.832	1.778	1.766	1.767
	methylene chloride	1.853	1.784	1.768	1.772
	methyl chloride	1.892	1.806	1.785	1.781
CGe	methylgermane	1.963	1.979	—	1.945
CSe	methylselenide	1.985	1.966	—	1.959
CBr	bromoform	1.971	1.932	—	1.924
	methylene bromide	1.977	1.937	—	1.925
	carbon tetrabromide	1.980	1.935	—	1.930
	methyl bromide	2.000	1.953	—	1.934
CI	iodoform	2.187	2.176	—	2.120
	methyl iodide	2.194	2.179	—	2.136

Table 2-5: Effect of d Functions on Bond Distances in Molecules Incorporating Second-Row and Heavier Main-Group Elements with Expanded Valence Octets

molecule	bond	3-21G	3-21G$^{(*)}$	6-31G*	expt.
phosphorous pentafluoride	PF_{ax}	1.604	1.566	1.568	1.577
	PF_{eq}	1.580	1.538	1.535	1.534
trimethylphospine oxide	PO	1.598	1.478	1.474	1.479
	PC	1.849	1.805	1.819	1.813
sulfur dioxide	SO	1.419	1.419	1.414	1.431
dimethylsulfoxide	SO	1.678	1.490	1.485	1.485
	SC	1.862	1.791	1.796	1.799
sulfur tetrafluoride	SF_{ax}	1.677	1.617	1.632	1.646
	SF_{eq}	1.616	1.550	1.544	1.545
sulfur trioxide	SO	1.532	1.411	1.405	1.420
dimethylsulfone	SO	1.592	1.438	1.437	1.431
	SC	1.830	1.756	1.774	1.777
sulfur hexafluoride	SF	1.612	1.550	1.554	1.564
chlorine trifluoride	ClF_{ax}	1.757	1.676	1.672	1.698
	ClF_{eq}	1.673	1.601	1.579	1.598
chlorine pentafluoride	ClF_{ax}	1.696	1.599	1.590	1.571
	ClF_{eq}	1.715	1.624	1.630	1.669
arsenic pentafluoride	AsF_{ax}	1.682	1.694	—	1.711
	AsF_{eq}	1.659	1.672	—	1.656

Table 2-5: Effect of d Functions on Bond Distances in Molecules Incorporating Second-Row and Heavier Main-Group Elements with Expanded Valence Octets (continued)

molecule	bond	3-21G	3-21G$^{(*)}$	6-31G*	expt.
selenium dioxide	SeO	1.617	1.599	—	1.608
selenium tetrafluoride	SeF$_{ax}$	1.739	1.742	—	1.771
	SeF$_{eq}$	1.688	1.687	—	1.682
bromine trifluoride	BrF$_{ax}$	1.807	1.778	—	1.810
	BrF$_{eq}$	1.738	1.721	—	1.721
bromine pentafluoride	BrF$_{ax}$	1.713	1.704	—	1.689
	BrF$_{eq}$	1.757	1.733	—	1.774
iodine pentafluoride	IF$_{ax}$	1.836	1.845	—	1.844
	IF$_{eq}$	1.871	1.872	—	1.869

Figure 2-7: Bond Lengths in Molecules Incorporating Second Row, Main-Group Elements. □=3-21G, ○=3-21G$^{(*)}$,△=6-31G*

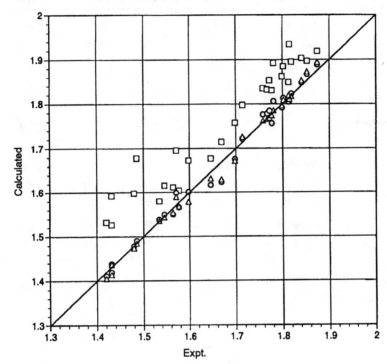

Table 2-6: Effect of d Functions on Electric Dipole Moments in Molecules Incorporating Second-Row Elements

heteroatom	molecule	3-21G	3-21G$^{(*)}$	6-31G*	expt.
silicon	Me_3SiH	0.49	0.53	0.51	0.53
	$MeSiH_3$	0.63	0.70	0.68	0.74
	Me_2SiH_2	0.64	0.70	0.67	0.75
	$EtSiH_3$	0.74	0.77	0.75	0.81
phosphorus	PH_3	1.24	0.87	0.88	0.58
	F_3PS	1.03	1.23	1.42	0.64
	$MePH_2$	1.39	1.21	1.27	1.10
	$EtPH_2$	1.55	1.32	1.32	1.17
	Me_3P	1.28	1.28	1.37	1.19
	Me_2PH	1.36	1.29	1.37	1.23
	F_3PO	1.48	1.75	1.96	1.76
sulfur	(thiophene structure)	1.34	0.76	0.90	0.55
	SF_4	2.21	1.37	1.00	0.63
	H_2S	1.82	1.41	1.41	0.97
	Me_2S	2.07	1.75	1.80	1.50
	$MeSH$	2.12	1.74	1.79	1.52
	$EtSH$	2.19	1.80	1.86	1.58
	SO_2	2.98	2.29	2.19	1.63
	F_2SO	3.17	2.40	2.22	1.63
	(thiirane structure)	2.81	2.12	2.31	1.85
	NSF	2.14	2.16	2.15	1.90
	$(CH_3)_2SO$	4.90	4.30	4.50	3.96
	$(CH_3)_2SO_2$	6.15	4.98	5.11	4.49
chlorine	$FClO_3$	0.33	0.47	0.50	0.02
	ClF_5	1.98	1.33	0.83	0.54
	ClF_3	1.38	1.15	0.85	0.55
	HCl	1.86	1.51	1.50	1.08
	$FClO_2$	0.96	2.55	2.33	1.72
	CH_3Cl	2.86	2.31	2.25	1.87

Figure 2-8: Dipole Moments in Molecules Incorporating Second Row, Main-Group Elements. □=3-21G, ○=3-21G$^{(*)}$, △=6-31G*

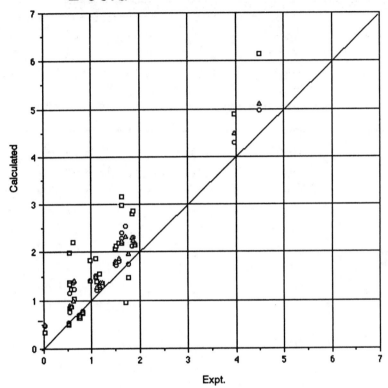

Table 2-7: Effect of d-functions on Bond Distances Connecting Heavy Atoms and Electric Dipole Moments in Molecules Incorporating Alkali and Alkaline-Earth Elements

molecule	bond distance			electric dipole moment		
	3-21G	3-21G(*)	expt.	3-21G	3-21G(*)	expt.
LiCl	2.112	2.091	2.021	8.14	7.77	7.13
LiBr	2.241	2.178	2.170	7.61	7.04	7.27
LiI	2.487	2.453	2.392	8.15	7.56	7.43
NaOH	1.870	1.857	1.95	5.47	5.39	
NaF	1.863	1.822	1.926	7.54	7.26	8.16
NaCl	2.420	2.378	2.361	10.16	9.46	9.00
NaBr	2.571	2.463	2.502	9.76	8.80	
NaI	2.829	2.737	2.711	10.50	9.41	
MgO	1.776	1.728	1.749	5.65	6.85	
MgF_2	1.722	1.701	1.77	0	0	0
KOH	2.230	2.170	2.212	7.49	6.80	
KF	2.218	2.138	2.171	9.36	8.50	8.60
KCl	2.829	2.787	2.667	12.63	11.65	10.27
KBr	2.998	2.881	2.821	12.55	11.15	10.41
KI	3.273	3.184	3.048	13.66	12.17	
RbOH	2.373	2.270	2.301	8.23	6.50	
RbF	2.351	2.239	2.270	9.96	8.09	8.55
RbCl	2.985	2.924	2.787	13.46	11.93	
RbBr	3.164	3.020	2.945	13.52	11.49	
RbI	3.446	3.329	3.177	14.74	12.70	

The way to understand the effect which electron correlation has on equilibrium structure, or more precisely on bond lengths, is to consider in a strictly operational sense how correlation is introduced "on top of" the Hartree-Fock description. Configuration interaction models are the easiest to grasp in this sense. Here, what is done is to find the best linear combination of determinants, the leading term in the linear combination being the Hartree-Fock determinant, and successive terms being determinants formed from the Hartree-Fock determinant by explicit promotions of one or more electrons, i.e.,

$$\psi^{\text{correlated}} = c_0 \, \psi^{\text{Hartree Fock}} + \sum_{ijk} \sum_{abc} c_{ijk}^{abc} \, \psi_{ijk}^{abc}$$

Here, i,j,k. . . . represent occupied molecular orbitals (in the Hartree-Fock determinant) and a,b,c. . . represent unoccupied (or virtual) molecular orbitals. The c's are unknown coefficients. A simple diagram helps to clarify the situation.

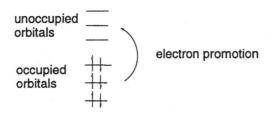

For molecules with sufficient (or excessive) electrons to make up all necessary 2-electron, 2-center bonds (normal covalent bonds), all of the occupied molecular orbitals will typically either be primarily bonding or primarily non-bonding. Conspicuously missing, will be molecular orbitals which are antibonding between neighboring atoms. On the other hand, in this case all of the unoccupied molecular orbitals will typically have antibonding components between neighboring atoms. Consider ethylene as an example. Here, the highest occupied molecular orbital corresponds to the CC π bond, while the lowest unoccupied orbital is the CC π^* orbital.

Lower energy filled molecular orbitals correspond to CH and CC σ bonds, and higher energy unfilled molecular orbitals are σ antibonding with respect to CC and/or CH linkages.

The result of electron promotion is clear: bonds will be weakened by removal of electrons from bonding molecular orbitals and further weakened by addition of these electrons to antibonding molecular orbitals. It must be that limiting Hartree-Fock bond lengths are typically shorter than experimental distances, and that inclusion of electron correlation leads to bond lengthening. Unfortunately, we cannot say with certainty whatever specific practical correlated methods will also exhibit such systematic behavior. Of course, in the limit of full correlation on a complete basis set, bond lengths will match exactly experimental values, but such approaches are not practical (see also **Section 2.8**).

2.7 Are d functions required for accurate geometry descriptions using correlated models, including density functional models?

We have previously suggested that Hartree-Fock models using split-valence basis sets generally provide reasonable descriptions of molecular equilibrium geometries. For molecules incorporating first-row elements only, even the simple 3-21G split-valence basis set is adequate, although as documented in **Section 2.5**, basis sets for second-row and heavier main-group elements need to be supplemented with d-type functions in order to provide consistent and reliable descriptions of geometry. Here we address a somewhat different question, mainly the importance of d-type functions for accurate geometry determinations using correlated methods, including density functional methods. We'll focus both on molecules comprising first-row elements only (where for Hartree-Fock models, d-functions are not usually viewed as greatly influencing geometry), and then on molecules incorporating second-row elements. There is very little experience with the performance of correlated models for molecules incorporating heavier (than second row) elements.

There is good reason to expect that d functions will be more important for correlated models than they will for Hartree-Fock models. Recall from our discussion in the previous section, that operationally electron correlation effects are taken into account either by (implicit or explicit) promotion of electrons from occupied molecular orbitals into unoccupied (virtual) molecular orbitals, i.e.,

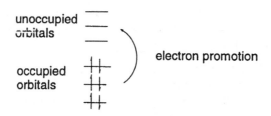

While occupied molecular orbitals for molecules containing light elements generally have only small contributions from d-type atomic orbitals (at least to the extent that they influence equilibrium geometry), many of the low energy virtual orbitals (which give rise to excited states) involve significant contributions from d-type functions. Thus, it would not be surprising to find that the overall effectiveness of correlated models would depend on whether or not d functions were available.

Central bond lengths in a small selection of two-heavy-atom molecules comprising first-row elements only are given in **Table 2-8**. Both the SVWN and B3LYP density functional models and the MP2 correlated model are examined with two different basis sets: 6-31G, which does not include d functions, and 6-31G*, which does include d functions on all heavy elements. While 6-31G is not a commonly-employed basis set (3-21G is simpler and less costly, and generally gives similar results with regard to equilibrium geometry), except for its lack of d-orbitals on heavy atoms it is identical to 6-31G*, and hence is appropriate for our purpose here. Experimental data has also been included for comparison.

The results are dramatic. While SVWN/6-31G*, B3LYP/6-31G* and MP2/6-31G* models provide good descriptions of the central bond lengths in these systems, none of these methods used in conjunction with the 6-31G basis set gives an acceptable account. As expected, inclusion of d functions leads to bond shortening. The differences are most apparent for systems with one or more highly electronegative atoms, or when multiple bonds are involved, and are fairly independent of the kind of correlation treatment (density functional or MP2).

The same comparisons are made for molecules incorporating one or two second-row elements in **Table 2-9**. The results are similar to those already provided for first-row systems for all three methods, in that conclusion of d functions leads to bond shortening. Of course, we have already made note of the fact that d functions are also necessary for accurate Hartree-Fock geometry descriptions for molecules incorporating second-row (and heavier main-group) elements (see **Section 2.5**).

Clearly, correlated models should not be applied to (equilibrium) geometry determination unless the underlying basis sets include functions of d-type symmetry. Use of smaller basis sets leads to unreliable results, and sometimes to structures which are significantly in error. A consequence of this is that, unlike Hartree-Fock models where use of small basis sets generally leads to quite good equilibrium geometries, there can be no simple (small basis set) correlated treatments, which lead to consistent (reliable) structural results.

2.8 Do theoretical models which account explicitly for electron correlation always provide more accurate descriptions of molecular equilibrium geometries than Hartree-Fock models which do not?

This question (and closely-related questions dealing with thermochemistry and conformational energy differences to be addressed later in this book; **Sections 4.3** and **6.3**) is important because of the prevailing attitude among computational chemists that the more expensive the method the better will be its results ("you get what you pay for"). While there is no doubt that in the limit of a complete basis set, methods that take full account of electron correlation (by way of complete configuration interaction or Møller-Plesset perturbation methods taken to infinite order) will provide more accurate descriptions than complete basis set Hartree-Fock methods, such methods are not practical, nor will they be in the foreseeable future. The real question is then whether "practical" correlated methods provide more accurate descriptions of equilibrium geometry than "practical" Hartree-Fock methods.

We consider four different theoretical models; Hartree-Fock models, SVWN and B3LYP density functional models and MP2 correlated models. For each model, two different basis sets are examined: 6-31G* which is among the

Table 2-8: Effect of d-Functions on Central Bond Distances in Molecules Incorporating First-Row Elements Only

molecule	SVWN/		B3LYP/		MP2/		expt.
	6-31G	6-31G*	6-31G	6-31G*	6-31G	6-31G*	
ethane	1.516	1.511	1.535	1.531	1.544	1.527	1.531
methylamine	1.433	1.443	1.460	1.465	1.478	1.465	1.471
methanol	1.429	1.399	1.452	1.419	1.471	1.424	1.421
methyl fluoride	1.413	1.364	1.434	1.383	1.454	1.392	1.383
hydrazine	1.353	1.404	1.403	1.437	1.438	1.439	1.449
hydrogen peroxide	1.515[a]	1.433	1.532[a]	1.456	1.569	1.467	1.452
fluorine	1.456	1.387	1.468	1.403	1.503	1.421	1.412
ethylene	1.334	1.329	1.336	1.331	1.351	1.337	1.339
formaldehyde	1.229	1.205	1.232	1.207	1.258	1.221	1.208
acetylene	1.216	1.211	1.211	1.205	1.232	1.218	1.203
nitrogen	1.123	1.110	1.118	1.106	1.154	1.131	1.098

a) Distorts to an incorrect *trans* planar structure.

Table 2-9: Effect of d-Functions on Central Bond Distances in Molecules Incorporating Second-Row Elements

molecule	SVWN/		B3LYP/		MP2/		expt.
	6-31G	6-31G*	6-31G	6-31G*	6-31G	6-31G*	
methylsilane	1.895	1.867	1.918	1.889	1.930	1.884	1.867
methyl phosphine	1.898	1.852	1.924	1.876	1.926	1.860	1.862
methanethiol	1.868	1.808	1.898	1.836	1.902	1.817	1.819
methyl chloride	1.843	1.773	1.878	1.804	1.883	1.778	1.781
disilane	2.336	2.321	2.369	2.351	2.383	2.338	2.327
silyl fluoride	1.698	1.606	1.704	1.613	1.710	1.619	1.596
silyl chloride	2.173	2.057	2.200	2.079	2.214	2.060	2.048
diphosphine	2.335	2.221	2.366	2.251	2.363	2.212	2.219
hydrogen disulfide	2.228	2.067	2.261	2.098	2.281	2.069	2.055
chlorine	2.180	2.012	2.206	2.042	2.229	2.015	1.988

simplest of polarization basis sets, and 6-311+G(2d,p) which has a triply-split valence representation with two sets of polarization functions and a single set of diffuse functions on heavy atoms, as well as a single set of polarization functions on hydrogen. The smaller of the two basis sets is routinely applicable to organic molecules; the larger basis set represents about as complete a representation which can presently be applied to small to medium size organic molecules. We have not considered smaller basis sets, in particular, 3-21G[(*)].Previous discussion (**Section 2.7**) points to the need for polarization (d-type) functions in the representation for density functional and correlated methods. Further evidence of this is found in the overall error statistics provided in **Appendix A**.

Two different data sets have been provided, the first for central bond lengths in two-heavy-atom hydrides (**Table 2-10** and **Figures 2-9 to 2-16**), and the second for bonds connecting heavy atoms in molecules incorporating second-row elements with expanded valence octets (**Table 2-11** and **Figures 2-17 to 2-24**). While the latter compounds are certainly not "typical" organic molecules, the fact that they may represent extremes in bonding perhaps justifies their inclusion here to provide an overview of performance.

All eight methods examined yield excellent descriptions of bond lengths connecting heavy atoms in two-heavy-atom molecules. Hartree-Fock models nearly always result in bond lengths which are shorter than experimental values, although the differences are typically quite small. (Large deviations occur in molecules such as hydrogen peroxide and fluorine, where two highly electronegative elements are involved.) As already outlined in **Section 2.6**, the reason for Hartree-Fock bond lengths being shorter than experimental distances follows from the way in which electron correlation is taken into account starting from the Hartree-Fock description. This involves either explicit or implicit promotion of electrons from filled molecular orbitals into empty (virtual) molecular orbitals, i.e.,

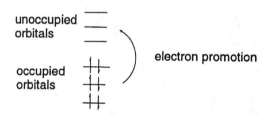

While filled molecular orbitals are typically either "bonding" or "non-bonding" in nature, unfilled orbitals are often "antibonding". Thus, removal of an electron from a filled (in the Hartree-Fock description) molecular orbital weakens bonding, as does addition of the electron to a previously unfilled molecular orbital.

B3LYP density functional models and MP2 models would not necessarily be expected to show similar behavior to Hartree-Fock models, and in fact limiting bond distances are both shorter and longer than experimental values. Surprisingly, the local density functional (SVWN) method results in bond lengths which are consistently shorter than experimental values (just like the Hartree-Fock models). We know of no way to rationalize this.

Table 2-10: Central Bond Lengths in Two-Heavy-Atom Hydrides

molecule	HF/ 6-31G*	HF/ 6-311+G(2d,p)	SVWN/ 6-31G*	SVWN/ 6-311+G(2d,p)	B3LYP/ 6-31G*	B3LYP/ 6-311+G(2d,p)	MP2/ 6-31G*	MP2/ 6-311+G(2d,p)	expt.
Li_2	2.812	2.784	2.735	2.698	2.725	2.704	2.673	2.782	2.673
LiOH	1.592	1.581	1.574	1.572	1.584	1.583	1.582	1.594	1.582
LiF	1.555	1.565	1.539	1.557	1.550	1.571	1.564	1.570	1.564
LiCl	2.072	2.035	2.040	2.004	2.055	2.024	2.021	2.069	2.021
B_2H_6	1.778	1.779	1.735	1.725	1.769	1.761	1.763	1.754	1.763
C_2H_2	1.185	1.180	1.211	1.200	1.205	1.196	1.203	1.218	1.203
C_2H_4	1.317	1.315	1.329	1.322	1.331	1.325	1.339	1.337	1.339
C_2H_6	1.527	1.525	1.511	1.508	1.531	1.529	1.531	1.527	1.531
HCN	1.133	1.124	1.162	1.150	1.157	1.146	1.153	1.177	1.153
HNC	1.154	1.145	1.181	1.166	1.177	1.165	1.169	1.187	1.169
CH_2NH	1.250	1.247	1.269	1.261	1.271	1.265	1.273	1.282	1.273
CH_3NH_2	1.453	1.453	1.443	1.443	1.465	1.467	1.471	1.465	1.471
CO	1.114	1.104	1.141	1.127	1.138	1.126	1.128	1.151	1.128
H_2CO	1.184	1.178	1.205	1.198	1.207	1.200	1.208	1.221	1.208
CH_3OH	1.400	1.399	1.399	1.402	1.419	1.424	1.421	1.424	1.421
CH_3F	1.365	1.364	1.364	1.374	1.383	1.394	1.383	1.392	1.383
CH_3SiH_3	1.888	1.878	1.867	1.858	1.889	1.880	1.867	1.884	1.867
HCP	1.515	1.511	1.546	1.537	1.543	1.537	1.540	1.562	1.540
CH_2PH	1.652	1.646	1.669	1.659	1.674	1.665	1.67	1.652	1.67

Table 2-10: Central Bond Lengths in Two-Heavy-Atom Hydrides (continued)

molecule	HF/ 6-31G*	HF/ 6-311+G(2d,p)	SVWN/ 6-31G*	SVWN/ 6-311+G(2d,p)	B3LYP/ 6-31G*	B3LYP/ 6-311+G(2d,p)	MP2/ 6-31G*	MP2/ 6-311+G(2d,p)	expt.
CH_3PH_2	1.861	1.856	1.852	1.843	1.876	1.870	1.862	1.860	1.862
CS	1.520	1.513	1.550	1.535	1.548	1.536	1.535	1.546	1.535
H_2CS	1.597	1.593	1.612	1.603	1.618	1.611	1.611	1.617	1.611
CH_3SH	1.817	1.819	1.808	1.803	1.836	1.834	1.819	1.817	1.819
CH_3Cl	1.785	1.792	1.773	1.771	1.804	1.807	1.781	1.778	1.781
N_2	1.078	1.067	1.110	1.095	1.106	1.092	1.131	1.114	1.098
N_2H_2	1.216	1.209	1.244	1.234	1.246	1.237	1.267	1.258	1.252
N_2H_4	1.413	1.412	1.404	1.404	1.437	1.436	1.439	1.437	1.449
HNO	1.175	1.168	1.204	1.196	1.208	1.201	1.237	1.226	1.212
NH_2OH	1.403	1.392	1.403	1.407	1.432	1.434	1.453	1.435	1.453
NP	1.455	1.449	1.500	1.488	1.495	1.485	1.537	1.525	1.491
H_2O_2	1.393	1.388	1.433	1.431	1.456	1.452	1.467	1.459	1.452
HOF	1.376	1.365	1.414	1.414	1.434	1.432	1.444	1.435	1.442
NaOH	1.922	1.946	1.893	1.919	1.916	1.946	1.934	1.976	1.95
MgO	1.738	1.727	1.729	1.730	1.743	1.745	1.733	1.751	1.749
SiO	1.487	1.480	1.527	1.516	1.524	1.515	1.544	1.533	1.510
HPO	1.460	1.449	1.502	1.488	1.500	1.488	1.519	1.504	1.512
HOCl	1.670	1.663	1.702	1.693	1.727	1.720	1.717	1.718	1.690
F_2	1.345	1.330	1.387	1.386	1.403	1.400	1.421	1.410	1.412

Table 2-10: Central Bond Lengths in Two-Heavy-Atom Hydrides (continued)

molecule	HF/		SVWN/		B3LYP/		MP2/		expt.
	6-31G*	6-311+G(2d,p)	6-31G*	6-311+G(2d,p)	6-31G*	6-311+G(2d,p)	6-31G*	6-311+G(2d,p)	
NaF	1.885	1.929	1.864	1.918	1.890	1.942	1.920	1.983	1.926
SiH_3F	1.594	1.586	1.606	1.607	1.613	1.616	1.619	1.612	1.596
ClF	1.613	1.607	1.642	1.642	1.662	1.663	1.661	1.665	1.628
Na_2	3.130	3.198	2.962	2.979	3.039	3.055	3.170	3.182	3.078
NaCl	2.397	2.391	2.333	2.327	2.368	2.368	2.393	2.400	2.361
Si_2H_6	2.353	2.373	2.321	2.318	2.351	2.357	2.338	2.358	2.327
SiH_3Cl	2.067	2.072	2.057	2.054	2.079	2.080	2.060	2.075	2.048
P_2	1.859	1.856	1.906	1.893	1.904	1.895	1.936	1.935	1.893
P_2H_4	2.214	2.228	2.221	2.213	2.251	2.250	2.212	2.235	2.219
H_2S_2	2.064	2.075	2.067	2.060	2.098	2.096	2.069	2.092	2.055
Cl_2	1.990	2.000	2.012	2.000	2.042	2.035	2.015	2.029	1.988

40

Figure 2-9: Comparison of Calculated and Experimental Bond Distances in Two-Heavy Atom Molecules: HF/6-31G* Model

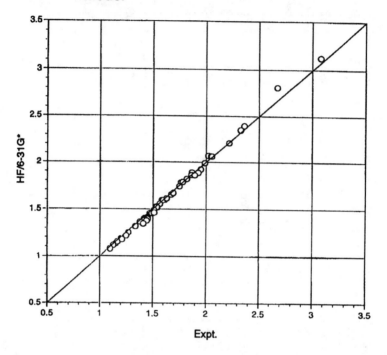

Figure 2-10: Comparison of Calculated and Experimental Bond Distances in Two-Heavy Atom Molecules: HF/6-311+G(2d,p) Model

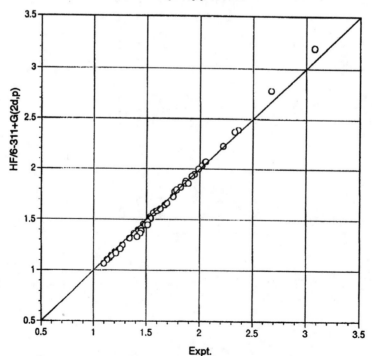

Figure 2-11: Comparison of Calculated and Experimental Bond Distances in Two-Heavy Atom Molecules: SVWN/6-31G* Model

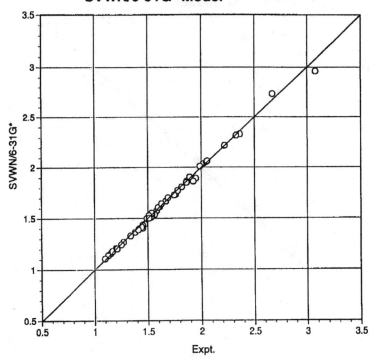

Figure 2-12: Comparison of Calculated and Experimental Bond Distances in Two-Heavy Atom Molecules: SWVN/6-311+G(2d,p) Model

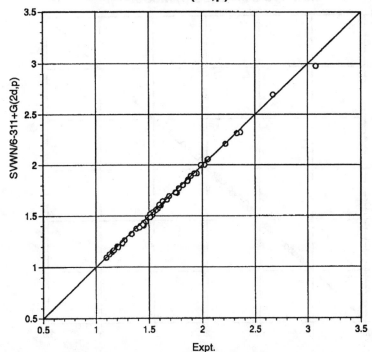

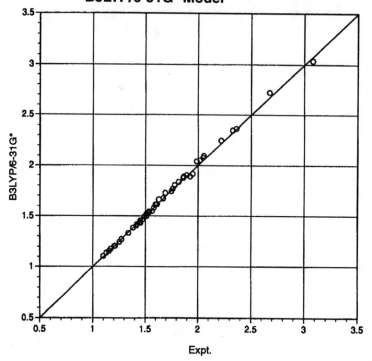

Figure 2-13: Comparison of Calculated and Experimental Bond Distances in Two-Heavy Atom Molecules: B3LYP/6-31G* Model

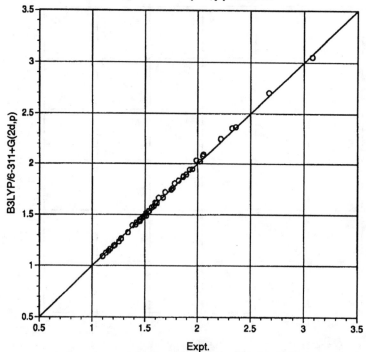

Figure 2-14: Comparison of Calculated and Experimental Bond Distances in Two-Heavy Atom Molecules: B3LYP/6-311+G(2d,p) Model

Figure 2-15: Comparison of Calculated and Experimental Bond Distances in Two-Heavy Atom Molecules: MP2/6-31G* Model

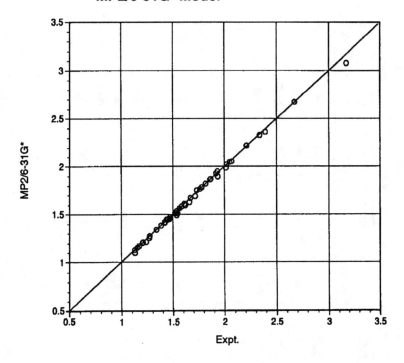

Figure 2-16: Comparison of Calculated and Experimental Bond Distances in Two-Heavy Atom Molecules: MP2/6-311+G(2d,p) Model

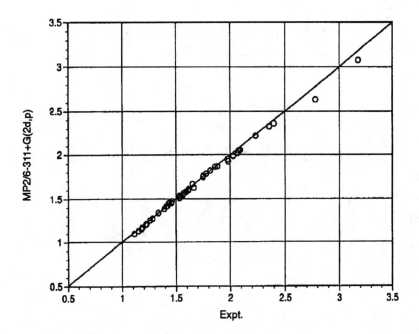

Table 2-11: Bond Lengths in Hypervalent Molecules

molecule	bond length	HF/		SVWN/		B3LYP/		MP2/		expt.
		6-31G*	6-311+G(2d,p)	6-31G*	6-311+G(2d,p)	6-31G*	6-311+G(2d,p)	6-31G*	6-311+G(2d,p)	
PF$_5$	PF$_{eq}$	1.535	1.516	1.562	1.549	1.569	1.556	1.569	—	1.534
	PF$_{ax}$	1.568	1.560	1.586	1.584	1.598	1.595	1.598	—	1.577
(CH$_3$)$_3$PO	PO	1.474	1.461	1.501	1.487	1.501	1.489	1.507	—	1.479
	PC	1.819	1.811	1.811	1.799	1.836	1.826	1.820	—	1.813
F$_3$PO	PO	1.425	1.413	1.456	1.442	1.455	1.442	1.459	1.447	1.436
	PF	1.526	1.505	1.553	1.539	1.559	1.546	1.561	1.541	1.524
F$_3$PS	PS	1.874	1.874	1.879	1.870	1.890	1.885	1.872	1.882	1.866
	PF	1.535	1.515	1.564	1.552	1.570	1.558	1.571	1.551	1.538
SO$_2$	SO	1.414	1.400	1.467	1.447	1.464	1.446	1.478	1.460	1.431
(CH$_3$)$_2$SO	SO	1.485	1.471	1.504	1.494	1.511	1.501	1.512	—	1.485
	SC	1.796	1.796	1.813	1.799	1.838	1.831	1.809	—	1.799
SF$_4$	SF$_{eq}$	1.544	1.521	1.588	1.579	1.595	1.583	1.588	1.567	1.545
	SF$_{ax}$	1.632	1.630	1.655	1.671	1.672	1.690	1.665	1.679	1.646
F$_2$SO	SO	1.409	1.395	1.448	1.430	1.446	1.429	1.446	1.431	1.413
	SF	1.571	1.554	1.619	1.623	1.629	1.634	1.627	1.625	1.585
NSF	SN	1.431	1.419	1.462	1.446	1.459	1.444	1.444	1.437	1.448
	SF	1.615	1.613	1.670	1.692	1.680	1.711	1.700	1.744	1.643
SO$_3$	SO	1.405	1.390	1.455	1.435	1.453	1.435	1.459	1.443	1.420
(CH$_3$)$_2$SO$_2$	SO	1.437	1.420	1.467	1.449	1.470	1.453	1.469	—	1.431
	SC	1.774	1.769	1.783	1.768	1.810	1.800	1.785	—	1.777

Table 2-11: Bond Lengths in Hypervalent Molecules (continued)

molecule	bond length	HF/		SVWN/		B3LYP/		MP2/		expt.
		6-31G*	6-311+G(2d,p)	6-31G*	6-311+G(2d,p)	6-31G*	6-311+G(2d,p)	6-31G*	6-311+G(2d,p)	
SF_6	SF	1.554	1.537	1.587	1.580	1.601	1.593	1.595	—	1.564
F_4SO	SO	1.404	1.388	1.439	1.419	1.440	1.420	1.438	—	1.403
	SF_{eq}	1.537	1.511	1.586	1.569	1.595	1.576	1.590	—	1.552
	SF_{ax}	1.582	1.571	1.614	1.618	1.629	1.632	1.626	—	1.575
ClF_3	ClF_{ax}	1.672	1.680	1.708	1.727	1.728	1.750	1.720	1.746	1.698
	ClF_{eq}	1.579	1.564	1.641	1.636	1.651	1.644	1.638	1.632	1.598
ClF_5	ClF_{ax}	1.590	1.567	1.635	1.633	1.653	1.646	1.645	—	1.571
	ClF_{eq}	1.630	1.628	1.682	1.703	1.699	1.720	1.690	—	1.669
$FClO_2$	ClO	1.419	1.396	1.468	1.444	1.469	1.446	1.456	1.442	1.418
	ClF	1.617	1.623	1.716	1.751	1.735	1.776	1.759	1.821	1.696
$FClO_3$	ClO	1.402	1.377	1.449	1.423	1.453	1.428	1.442	1.422	1.404
	ClF	1.579	1.561	1.661	1.672	1.678	1.693	1.683	1.696	1.619

Figure 2-17: Comparison of Calculated and Experimental Bond Distances in Hypervalent Molecules: HF/6-31G* Model

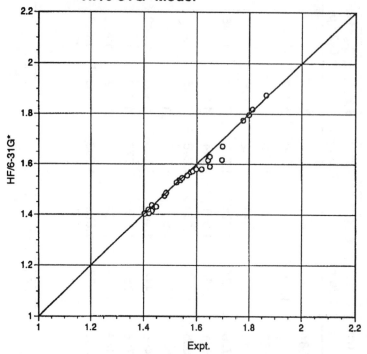

Figure 2-18: Comparison of Calculated and Experimental Bond Distances in Hypervalent Molecules: HF/6-311+G(2d,p) Model

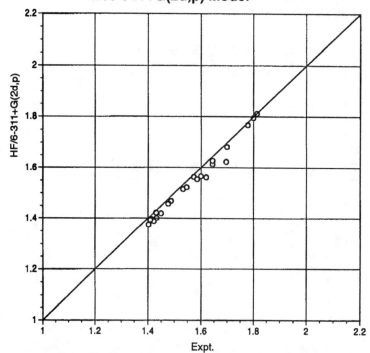

Figure 2-19: Comparison of Calculated and Experimental Bond Distances in Hypervalent Molecules: SVWN/6-31G* Model

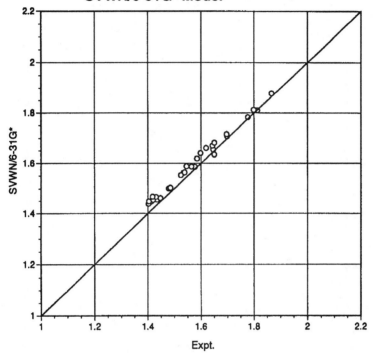

Figure 2-20: Comparison of Calculated and Experimental Bond Distances in Hypervalent Molecules: SVWN/6-311+G(2d,p) Model

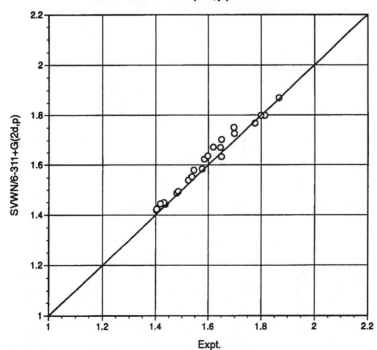

48

Figure 2-21: Comparison of Calculated and Experimental Bond Distances in Hypervalent Molecules: B3LYP/6-31G* Model

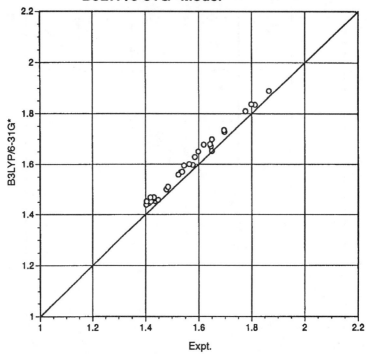

Figure 2-22: Comparison of Calculated and Experimental Bond Distances in Hypervalent Molecules: B3LYP/6-311+G(2d,p) Model

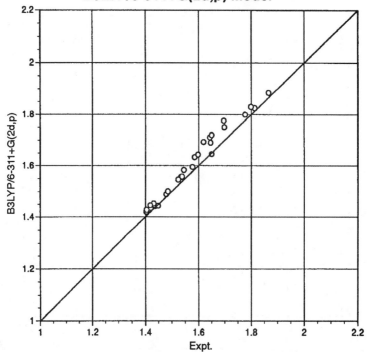

Figure 2-23: **Comparison of Calculated and Experimental Bond Distances in Hypervalent Molecules: MP2/6-31G* Model**

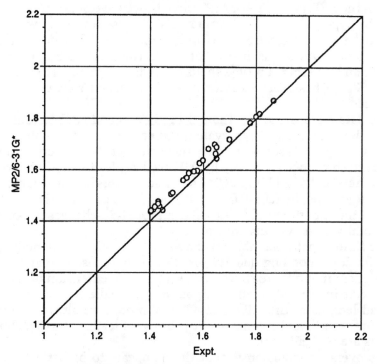

Figure 2-24: **Comparison of Calculated and Experimental Bond Distances in Hypervalent Molecules: MP2/6-311+G(2d,p) Model**

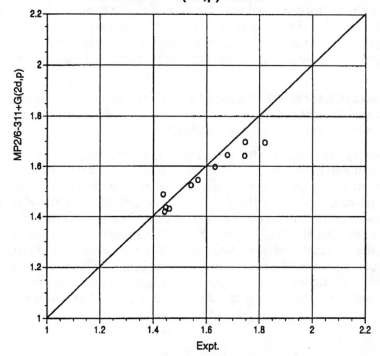

The hypervalent compounds (**Table 2-11** and **Figures 2-17** to **2-24**) provide a somewhat different perspective. Here, Hartree-Fock models actually provide significantly better descriptions of bond distances than either SVWN or B3LYP density functional models or the MP2 correlated model. To ascertain whether this is due at least in part to an inadequate basis set rather than to deficiencies inherent to the SVWN, B3LYP or MP2 models, we have obtained structures for a variety of hypervalent sulfur compounds at these levels (as well as at the Hartree-Fock level) using the 6-311+G(3df,2p) basis set. This incorporates three supplementary d type shells (instead of two in the 6-311+G(2d,p) basis set), an f-type shell and two sets of p-type shells on hydrogen (instead of a single set in the 6-311+G(2d,p) basis set). Structures for a few normal-valent compounds are also provided.

The data are provided in **Table 2-12**. SVWN and B3LYP results parallel each other. Bond lengths in hypervalent molecules previously obtained using the 6-311+G(2d,p) basis set were consistently longer than experimental values and these are shortened (typically by 0.01-0.02 Å), leading to improved agreement. The residual (6-311+G(3df,2p) basis set) errors are still large in some cases, but now typically 0.01-0.02Å, with nearly all calculated bond distances longer than the experimental values. Except for H_2S_2, changes in bond distances in normal-valent systems are smaller.

The limited data available for the MP2/6-311+G(3df,2p) model parallels that for the corresponding density functional methods, insofar as bonds in hypervalent compounds are shortened as a result of extension of the basis set and the effects in normal-valent compounds are smaller.

Bond lengths at the HF/6-311+G(2d,p) model are already shorter than experimental values and extension of the basis set leads to further shortening. The effects are typically small.

The overall conclusion is that there appears to be little advantage in using correlated models (including density functional models) for equilibrium geometry calculations. The performance of Hartree-Fock models with medium to large basis sets is quite good for diverse molecular systems, and actually superior to the performance of correlated models for some systems. There are cases where correlated models yield noticeably better equilibrium geometries, for example, for bonds involving two highly-electronegative elements, but these are relatively infrequent, and more important easily anticipated.

2.9 It is always necessary to utilize "exact" equilibrium geometries in carrying out thermochemical comparisons, or will geometries obtained from lower-level calculations suffice?

This is a very important question given that optimization of equilibrium structure can easily require one or even two orders of magnitude more computation than an energy (property) calculation at a single geometry. Rephrased, the question might read: *"Is the substantial added effort required to produce a proper optimized structure effort well spent?"* We address the issue here by reference to several series of simple thermochemical comparisons. (**Chapter 4** discusses the rationale behind subdividing thermochemical comparisons into a number of categories.) We first examine hydrogenation reactions and stability comparisons among structural isomers, to illustrate processes in which only the total number of electron pairs is conserved and not the numbers of each

Table 2-12: Bond Lengths in Sulfur Compounds

molecule	bond length	HF/	SVWN/	B3LYP/	MP2/	expt.
			6-311+G(3df,2p)			
CS	CS	1.510	1.532	1.533	1.537	1.535
H_2CS	CS	1.589	1.598	1.607	1.609	1.611
CH_3SH	CS	1.810	1.794	1.825	1.809	1.819
H_2S_2	SS	2.053	2.038	2.075	2.053	2.055
SO_2	SO	1.393	1.438	1.436	1.446	1.431
$(CH_3)_2SO$	SO	1.459	1.482	1.489	—	1.485
	SC	1.788	1.788	1.819	—	1.799
SF_4	SF_{eq}	1.512	1.563	1.567	—	1.545
	SF_{ax}	1.614	1.657	1.668	—	1.646
F_2SO	SO	1.389	1.423	1.422	1.422	1.413
	SF	1.540	1.601	1.611	1.598	1.585
NSF	SN	1.415	1.441	1.439	1.431	1.448
	SF	1.588	1.695	1.674	1.686	1.643
SO_3	SO	1.383	1.426	1.425	1.429	1.420
$(CH_3)_2SO_2$	SO	1.411	1.440	1.443	—	1.431
	SC	1.762	1.758	1.789	—	1.777
SF_6	SF	1.528	1.566	1.577	—	1.564
F_4SO	SO	1.381	1.411	1.412	—	1.403
	SF_{eq}	1.501	1.552	1.559	—	1.522
	SF_{ax}	1.561	1.601	1.615	—	1.575

kind of bond or lone pair. Next, we consider bond separation reactions and reactions which relate proton affinities of nitrogen bases relative to ammonia as a standard, to illustrate *isodesmic* processes, that is, reactions in which the total number of each kind of chemical bond is conserved and only the local environments are altered. Finally, we consider a special case of *isodesmic* reactions involving the comparison of the enegetics of isomers which differ only in the position of substituents. Examples of this are contained in comparisons of structural isomers, e.g., isobutene vs. *trans* 2-butene, or in stereochemistry, e.g., *trans* 2-butene vs. *cis* 2-butene, but our focus now is on reactions leading to different regio- and stereoproducts.

For each series, comparisons are made using Hartree-Fock, density functional (SVWN and B3LYP) and correlated (MP2) calculations, all with the 6-31G* basis set, and using three different sets of equilibrium structures (AM1, HF/3-21G(*) and "exact"). (Comparisons involving basicity have been carried out with 6-31G* instead of 3-21G geometries; see below.) Calculations with other Hartree-Fock or correlated level models should yield broadly similar conclusions, as should comparisons based on equilibrium structures from other low-level methods. Comparisons involving semi-empirical models are generally not favorable and are not addressed here. Commentary is available elsewhere.[1b]

While it is not our primary purpose to critically assess the performance of the various theoretical models with regard to reaction thermochemistry, we have also provided experimental data where available. This allows us to comment on the magnitudes of errors brought about from the use of approximate geometries, relative to errors inherent to a particular theoretical model in describing a particular type of reaction. Commentary about the performance of each of the models with regard to various thermochemical comparisons is made in **Chapter 4**, and much more complete documentation is available elsewhere.[1]

Hydrogenation-energy comparisons are presented in **Table 2-13** for HF/6-31G*, SVWN/6-31G*, B3LYP/6-31G* and MP2/6-31G* calculations. These are for two-heavy-atom molecules comprising first- and second-row elements only, and for which accurate experimental thermochemical data are available. First, it may be commented, that all theoretical models provide a reasonable description of hydrogenation thermochemistry. More relevant to the present discussion, the data show that use of approximate (AM1 or 3-21G(*)) geometries has little overall effect.

Relative energies of structural isomers are given in **Table 2-14** for HF/6-31G*, SVWN/6-31G*, B3LYP/6-31G* and MP2/6-31G* calculations. All models perform reasonably well, although the differences between them noted here are generally larger than those for hydrogenation energy comparisons (**Table 2-13**). The interested reader is directed elsewhere for further extensive commentary.[1] As before, choice of equilibrium geometry is of little consequence. Errors incurred are typically on the order of 1-2 kcal/mol, generally much less than deviations between calculated and experimental isomer energy differences.

Energies of bond separation reactions are provided in **Table 2-15** for the same theoretical models. As will be pointed out in **Section 4.2**, because bond separation reactions are generally well described even using rather simple levels of (*ab initio*) calculation, they may be employed in conjunction with experimental thermochemical data (or with results from high-level calculations) to yield accurate estimates of heats of formation. As with the previous two sets of comparisons, the results show very little sensitivity to choice of geometry.

The basicity comparisons in **Table 2-16** provide further encouragement for the use of approximate equilibrium geometries. Calculated relative basicities involving "exact" geometries, as well as those from AM1 geometries, are in very good agreement with experiment. (It is known, however, that basicities obtained using HF/3-21G geometries are sometimes significantly in error. This is due to the fact that the 3-21G model generally underestimates the degree of pyramidalization at nitrogen in the neutral bases. This also adversely affects electric dipole moments (see **Section 2.12**) and inversion barriers (see **Section 6.5**) calculated assuming 3-21G geometries. 6-31G* geometries have been substituted for 3-21G structures for these comparisons.)

Finally, relative energies of different regio- and stereoproducts resulting from Diels-Alder cycloadditions of substituted cyclopentadienes with acrylonitrile both as a function of underlying model (HF/6-31G*, SVWN/6-31G* and B3LYP/6-31G*) and of geometry (AM1, 3-21G[*] and "exact") are provided in **Table 2-17**. These illustrate the subtle but chemically important effects of positional changes on reaction thermochemistry. As before, the different theoretical models lead to similar effects which are little altered by exact choice of geometry.

The overall recommendation is to make use of either semi-empirical or low-level *ab initio* equilibrium geometries in constructing thermochemical comparisons based on higher-level models. While some caution is clearly needed in dealing with systems where certain calculation levels are known to produce incorrect geometries, e.g., 3-21G calculations on amines, in general the errors resulting from the use of approximate geometries are very small.

2.10 Do thermochemical comparisons involving anions require equilibrium geometries obtained using diffuse functions, or will geometries obtained from the underlying non-diffuse basis set suffice?

It is well known that diffuse functions in *ab initio* and correlated calculations significantly lower the total energies of anions and radical anions, and as such are likely to be important in the description of such quantities as acidities and oxidation/reduction potentials. Addition of diffuse functions to the basis set also leads to a significant increase in computational resources required, due both to an increase in total number of basis functions and to the fact that interaction integrals involving diffuse functions fall off only very slowly and therefore often may not be discarded. Given that structure optimization is generally the major time consuming component in a computational investigation, it is legitimate to ask to what extent diffuse functions significantly alter geometry. More to the point, can thermochemical comparisons which require diffuse basis sets for their proper description be made assuming geometries obtained from basis sets which do not incorporate diffuse functions?

A single example makes the point. Acidities of a variety of carbon acids, relative to the acidity of methane as a standard, are provided in **Table 2-18**. These have been evaluated using Hartree-Fock, density functional (SVWN and

Table 2-13: Effect of Choice of Geometry on Energies of Hydrogenation

hydrogenation reaction	HF/6-31G*//			SVWN/6-31G*//		
	AM1	3-21G$^{(*)}$	6-31G*	AM1	3-21G$^{(*)}$	SVWN/6-31G*
$Li_2 + H_2 \rightarrow 2LiH$	—	20	20	—	16	16
$LiOH + H_2 \rightarrow LiH + H_2O$	—	24	24	—	32	23
$LiF + H_2 \rightarrow LiH + HF$	—	49	49	—	55	40
$LiCl + H_2 \rightarrow LiH + HCl$	—	60	60	—	56	55
$CH_3CH_3 + H_2 \rightarrow 2CH_4$	−23	−22	−22	−21	−18	−20
$CH_3NH_2 + H_2 \rightarrow CH_4 + NH_3$	−29	−27	−27	−25	−22	−29
$CH_3OH + H_2 \rightarrow CH_4 + H_2O$	−29	−28	−27	−26	−24	−33
$CH_3F + H_2 \rightarrow CH_4 + HF$	−18	−23	−23	−12	−20	−36
$CH_3SiH_3 + H_2 \rightarrow CH_4 + SiH_4$	−16	−13	−13	−12	−8	−10
$CH_3SH + H_2 \rightarrow CH_4 + H_2S$	−25	−22	−22	−21	−17	−20
$CH_3Cl + H_2 \rightarrow CH_4 + HCl$	−24	−22	−22	−23	−19	−21
$NH_2NH_2 + H_2 \rightarrow 2NH_3$	−52	−45	−46	−45	−37	−50
$HOOH + H_2 \rightarrow 2H_2O$	−90	−84	−82	−80	−69	−87
$NaOH + H_2 \rightarrow H_2O + NaH$	—	10	10	—	13	3
$HOCl + H_2 \rightarrow H_2O + HCl$	−66	−64	−64	−58	−54	−65
$F_2 + H_2 \rightarrow 2HF$	−118	−127	−126	−89	−106	−138
$NaF + H_2 \rightarrow HF + NaH$	—	33	33	—	34	19
$SiH_3F + H_2 \rightarrow HF + SiH_4$	34	30	30	37	30	13
$ClF + H_2 \rightarrow HF + HCl$	−68	−73	−73	−85	−63	−81
$Na_2 + H_2 \rightarrow 2NaH$	—	40	40	—	34	35
$NaCl + H_2 \rightarrow NaH + HCl$	—	59	60	—	51	50
$SiH_3SiH_3 + H_2 \rightarrow 2SiH_4$	−13	−12	−12	−6	−2	−4
$SiH_3Cl + H_2 \rightarrow SiH_4 + HCl$	14	16	16	14	17	14
$PH_2PH_2 + H_2 \rightarrow 2PH_3$	−26	−11	−11	−17	−4	−6
$HSSH + H_2 \rightarrow 2H_2S$	−23	−21	−21	−16	−13	−16
$Cl_2 + H_2 \rightarrow 2HCl$	−53	−50	−50	−48	−43	−45
$CH_2=CH_2 + 2H_2 \rightarrow 2CH_4$	−67	−66	−66	−78	−72	−73
$CH_2=NH + 2H_2 \rightarrow CH_4 + NH_3$	−64	−60	−61	−72	−69	−73
$CH_2=O + 2H_2 \rightarrow CH_4 + H_2O$	−58	−54	−54	−66	−60	−69
$CH_2=S + 2H_2 \rightarrow CH_4 + H_2S$	−72	−64	−64	−78	−66	−66
$HN=NH + 2H_2 \rightarrow 2NH_3$	−80	−74	−76	−86	−77	−91
$HN=O + 2H_2 \rightarrow NH_3 + H_2O$	−102	−98	−98	−107	−97	−113
$O=O + 2H_2 \rightarrow 2H_2O$	−108	−99	−94	−134	−107	−125
$HP=O + 2H_2 \rightarrow H_2O + PH_3$	−53	−50	−50	−55	−49	−58

55

Reactions

B3LYP/6-31G*//			MP2/6-31G*//			
AM1	3-21G(*)	B3LYP/6-31G*	AM1	3-21G(*)	MP2/6-31G*	expt.
—	16	16	—	24	24	20
—	33	53	—	34	35	35
—	57	57	—	57	58	48
—	59	59	—	64	64	60
−23	−20	−19	−18	−17	−16	−19
−26	−23	−24	−25	−22	−23	−26
−26	−24	−24	−27	−25	−25	−30
−11	−19	−18	−14	−22	−21	−29
−14	−10	−10	−10	−6	−6	−6
−23	−19	−19	−18	−15	−15	−19
−23	−19	−19	−19	−17	−26	−22
−47	−38	−40	−49	−40	−42	−48
−82	−79	−69	−90	−75	−75	−86
—	14	14	—	18	19	21
−56	−54	−54	−57	−55	−55	−65
−88	−104	−105	−98	−116	−116	−133
—	37	37	—	39	66	35
40	32	33	43	34	56	48
−56	−62	−62	−57	−65	−83	−77
—	36	34	—	42	42	29
—	55	55	—	62	62	52
−6	−6	−6	−6	−4	−4	−5
14	17	17	19	21	21	33
−17	−7	−6	−17	−3	−3	−4
−16	−15	−15	−16	−13	−13	−14
−48	−42	−42	−48	−43	−43	−46
−66	−63	−62	−60	−58	−58	−57
−60	−55	−55	−56	−52	−52	−64
−52	−48	−48	−49	−46	−46	−59
−67	−57	−57	−58	−49	−49	−54
−73	−65	−67	−73	−64	−66	−68
−94	−85	−86	−97	−86	−87	−103
−118	−92	−92	−130	−97	−98	−125
−43	−38	−38	−35	−31	−47	−105

Table 2-13: Effect of Choice of Geometry on Energies of Hydrogenation

hydrogenation reaction	HF/6-31G*//			SVWN/6-31G*//		
	AM1	3-21G$^{(*)}$	6-31G*	AM1	3-21G$^{(*)}$	SVWN/6-31G*
HC≡CH + 3H$_2$ → 2CH$_4$	−122	−121	−121	−146	−137	−138
HC≡N + 3H$_2$ → CH$_4$ + NH$_3$	−82	−77	−78	−105	−97	−104
C$^-$≡O$^+$ + 3H$_2$ → CH$_4$ + H$_2$O	−63	−55	−55	−94	−84	−94
HC≡P + 3H$_2$ → CH$_4$ + PH$_3$	−112	−99	−99	−126	−104	−106
C$^-$≡S$^+$ + 3H$_2$ → CH$_4$ + H$_2$S	−122	−112	−111	−149	−129	−131
N≡N + 3H$_2$ → 2NH$_3$	−33	−26	−28	−63	−54	−67
P≡N + 3H$_2$ → NH$_3$ + PH$_3$	−88	−78	−79	−101	−83	−90
Si$^-$≡O$^+$ + 3H$_2$ → H$_2$O + SiH$_4$	−57	−48	−48	−54	−45	−53
P≡P + 3H$_2$ → 2PH$_3$	−102	−57	−57	−109	−55	−57

Reactions (continued)

B3LYP/6-31G*//			MP2/6-31G*//			
AM1	3-21G(*)	B3LYP/6-31G*	AM1	3-21G(*)	MP2/6-31G*	expt.
−122	−117	−116	−109	−105	−104	−105
−79	−73	−74	−64	−61	−60	−76
−65	−57	−57	−53	−48	−48	−63
−106	−87	−86	−88	−68	−67	−67
−122	−106	−106	−107	−92	−92	−91
−33	−26	−28	−18	−14	−13	−37
−78	−62	−63	−58	−38	−36	−45
−36	−29	−29	−22	−17	−16	−32
−94	−41	−41	−77	−20	−18	−44

Table 2-14 Effect of Choice of Geometry on Relative Energies of Structural

formula	molecule	HF/6-31G*//			SVWN/6-31G*//		
		AM1	3-21G(*)	6-31G*	AM1	3-21G(*)	SVWN/ 6-31G*
CHN	hydrogen cyanide	0	0	0	0	0	0
	hydrogen isocyanide	12.2	12.4	12.5	18.0	16.6	16.9
CH_2N_2	diazomethane	0	0	0	0	0	0
	diazirine	6.0	8.8	4.8	13.4	14.3	13.1
CH_2O	formaldehyde	0	0	0	0	0	0
	hydroxymethylene	51.0	52.6	52.0	60.2	59.7	59.3
CH_3NO	formamide	0	0	0	0	0	0
	nitrosomethane	63.2	65.3	63.5	65.5	63.4	63.4
CH_3NO_2	nitromethane	0	0	0	0	0	0
	methyl nitrite	−3.8	−4.3	−4.2	9.3	5.0	4.6
$C_2H_2Cl_2$	1,1-dichloroethylene	0	0	0	0	0	0
	cis 1,2-dichloroethylene	−2.1	−2.5	−2.5	−2.2	−1.6	−2.0
	trans 1,2-dichloroethylene	−2.2	−2.8	−2.8	−1.1	−0.6	−0.9
C_2H_3N	acetonitrile	0	0	0	0	0	0
	methyl isocyanide	21.0	20.9	24.1	25.4	25.3	25.3
C_2H_4O	acetaldehyde	0	0	0	0	0	0
	oxacyclopropane	29.7	33.4	30.5	21.5	23.4	21.5
$C_2H_4O_2$	acetic acid	0	0	0	0	0	0
	methyl formate	19.6	13.5	13.3	13.4	14.2	13.4
$C_2H_5NO_2$	glycine	0	0	0	0	0	0
	nitroethane	79.6	84.7	81.6	52.7	52.3	53.8
C_2H_6O	ethanol	0	0	0	0	0	0
	dimethyl ether	8.0	7.2	6.9	7.0	7.5	6.0

Isomers

B3LYP/6-31G*//			MP2/6-31G*//			
AM1	3-21G(*)	B3LYP/ 6-31G*	AM1	3-21G(*)	MP2/ 6-31G*	expt.
0	0	0	0	0	0	0
17.3	16.4	16.6	21.4	19.8	21.0	14.5
0	0	0	0	0	0	0
12.3	12.4	11.7	7.4	6.8	6.1	5.3
0	0	0	0	0	0	0
58.1	57.6	57.3	62.4	61.6	61.2	54.9
0	0	0	0	0	0	0
62.4	59.2	68.2	67.2	60.7	60.7	62.4
0	0	0	0	0	0	0
4.9	0.9	0.9	8.2	4.2	3.7	2.0
0	0	0	0	0	0	0
−1.9	−2.0	−2.1	−1.3	−1.4	−1.5	0.2
−1.7	−1.9	−2.0	−0.8	−0.9	−1.0	0.5
0	0	0	0	0	0	0
24.4	23.9	26.7	28.7	27.4	28.5	20.9
0	0	0	0	0	0	0
26.7	28.5	27.5	27.2	27.7	27.2	26.2
0	0	0	0	0	0	0
12.0	11.7	11.8	14.2	14.1	14.2	18.0
0	0	0	0	0	0	0
59.7	58.4	59.8	63.6	59.7	61.7	69.7
0	0	0	0	0	0	0
6.0	6.0	5.4	8.8	8.7	8.5	12.1

Table 2-14 Effect of Choice of Geometry on Relative Energies of Structural

formula	molecule	HF/6-31G*//			SVWN/6-31G*//		
		AM1	3-21G(*)	6-31G*	AM1	3-21G(*)	SVWN/6-31G*
C₂H₆Si	vinylsilane	0	0	0	0	0	0
	1-methylsilaethylene	20.0	17.0	17.0	6.7	3.5	3.9
C₂H₆S	ethanethiol	0	0	0	0	0	0
	dimethylsulfide	0.8	0.2	0.2	0.3	0.0	0.1
C₂H₇N	ethylamine	0	0	0	0	0	0
	dimethylamine	6.0	5.4	5.5	4.8	5.3	4.8
C₂H₈Si	dimethylsilane	0	0	0	0	0	0
	ethylsilane	10.7	10.5	10.4	10.8	11.0	10.4
C₃H₄	propyne	0	0	0	0	0	0
	allene	0.7	2.0	2.0	−5.1	−4.9	−4.3
	cyclopropene	25.5	26.5	25.9	14.5	14.7	14.5
C₃H₄N₂	imidazole	0	0	0	0	0	0
	pyrazole	11.7	13.8	13.1	8.6	9.6	9.3
C₃H₆	propene	0	0	0	0	0	0
	cyclopropane	7.6	8.2	7.9	0.3	0.9	0.9
C₃H₆O	acetone	0	0	0	0	0	0
	propanal	6.2	6.4	6.3	7.2	7.7	8.8
	2-hydroxypropene	16.6	21.0	18.8	13.2	14.7	
	allyl alcohol	26.1	28.9	28.1	26.8	28.6	28.2
	methyl vinyl ether	30.5	34.9	29.1	23.7	25.5	23.7
	propylene oxide	32.0	35.8	32.9	23.6	25.8	23.8
	oxetane	31.7	35.6	33.2	25.6	27.9	25.4
C₄H₄N₂	pyrazine	0	0	0	0	0	0
	pyrimidine	−5.8	−6.5	−6.6	−3.7	−4.1	−4.0
	1,2-ethanedinitrile	−3.8	−5.1	−4.5	28.6	30.7	26.3
	pyridazine	20.6	21.2	20.7	19.5	18.4	18.4

Isomers (continued)

	B3LYP/6-31G*//			MP2/6-31G*//			
AM1	3-21G(*)	B3LYP/ 6-31G*	AM1	3-21G(*)	MP2/ 6-31G*	expt.
0	0	0	0	0	0	0
12.6	8.9	9.1	12.4	8.3	8.5	11
0	0	0	0	0	0	0
0.1	−0.4	−0.6	−0.4	−1.1	−1.0	1.5
0	0	0	0	0	0	0
5.0	4.9	4.9	6.6	6.2	6.4	6.9
0	0	0	0	0	0	0
11.3	11.8	10.8	10.9	11.0	11.6	13
0	0	0	0	0	0	0
−3.7	−2.8	−2.7	3.4	4.3	4.8	1.6
21.1	21.7	21.5	21.6	22.6	22.9	21.7
0	0	0	0	0	0	0
9.6	10.2	10.0	9.9	10.3	9.8	12.7
0	0	0	0	0	0	0
7.4	7.6	7.7	4.2	4.2	4.4	6.9
0	0	0	0	0	0	0
6.4	6.5	6.9	6.0	6.4	6.2	6.5
15.7	17.6	17.0	17.6	19.0	18.4	7.7
27.0	28.8	28.1	28.8	29.9	29.2	21.6
25.2	26.6	26.1	29.8	31.0	30.1	25.6
28.8	30.6	29.6	28.8	29.5	29.0	29.5
30.7	32.7	31.8	32.5	33.9	32.9	30.8
0	0	0	0	0	0	0
−3.9	−4.2	−4.1	−3.5	−3.9	−3.7	0.1
10.5	10.0	10.0	0.6	0.8	−2.2	3.3
20.3	18.4	18.6	21.1	18.2	18.4	19.7

Table 2-14 Effect of Choice of Geometry on Relative Energies of Structural

formula	molecule	HF/6-31G*//			SVWN/6-31G*//		
		AM1	3-21G$^{(*)}$	6-31G*	AM1	3-21G$^{(*)}$	SVWN/6-31G*
C_4H_6	1,3–butadiene	0	0	0	0	0	0
	2-butyne	9.6	6.5	6.5	9.4	8.4	7.3
	cyclobutene	12.8	13.4	12.6	3.4	3.6	2.6
	1,2-butadiene	13.5	12.8	12.7	9.3	8.6	8.9
	1-butyne	14.4	13.0	12.9	17.5	16.7	16.5
	methylenecyclopropane	20.3	20.5	20.3	11.2	9.5	11.0
	bicyclo[1.1.0]butane	32.5	31.4	30.0	15.6	13.3	12.6
	1-methylcyclopropene	34.6	33.0	32.4	23.5	22.7	22.5
C_4H_8	isobutene	0	0	0	0	0	0
	trans 2-butene	0.8	0.2	0.2	1.1	0.7	0.8
	cis 2-butene	2.6	1.8	1.8	1.4	1.4	1.6
	skew 1-butene	3.2	3.0	2.9	5.3	5.1	4.6
	methylcyclopropane	9.1	9.5	9.2	3.0	2.9	3.4
	cyclobutane	8.2	9.2	9.4	2.6	2.8	1.7
$C_4H_8O_2$	1,3-dioxane	0	0	0	0	0	0
	1,4-dioxane	4.6	6.0	5.8	4.9	5.8	5.9
C_4H_{10}	isobutane	0	0	0	0	0	0
	n-butane	0.8	0.4	0.4	2.2	2.0	1.6
$C_6H_4F_2$	meta difluorobenzene	0	0	0	0	0	0
	para difluorobenzene	0.8	0.9	1.0	0.8	1.0	0.8
	ortho difluorobenzene	4.4	4.4	4.5	4.0	4.1	4.1
$C_{10}H_{18}$	*trans* decalin	0	0	0	0	0	0
	cis decalin	4.3	3.4	3.4	3.1	3.1	2.6

Isomers (continued)

| B3LYP/6-31G*// | | | MP2/6-31G*// | | | |
AM1	3-21G[(*)]	B3LYP/6-31G*	AM1	3-21G[(*)]	MP2/6-31G*	expt.
0	0	0	0	0	0	0
10.6	8.3	8.3	7.4	4.6	4.4	6.9
12.1	12.0	11.8	8.0	8.1	7.8	8.8
11.1	10.1	10.2	12.9	11.8	11.9	12.5
17.3	15.7	15.8	11.5	10.0	9.6	13.2
18.9	18.5	18.5	16.8	16.1	16.3	21.7
29.7	28.0	27.6	23.2	21.1	20.5	23.1
31.4	29.8	29.8	27.3	25.8	26.0	32.0
0	0	0	0	0	0	0
0.6	0.1	0.2	1.4	0.9	0.9	1.1
1.7	1.3	1.6	3.1	2.5	2.4	2.2
4.0	3.6	4.3	4.3	4.0	4.3	3.9
9.1	9.2	9.6	6.2	5.9	6.1	9.7
8.6	9.0	8.8	7.5	6.6	5.9	10.8
0	0	0	0	0	0	0
3.9	5.1	5.0	4.8	5.7	6.0	7.6
0	0	0	0	0	0	0
1.1	0.7	0.6	2.2	1.7	1.7	2.1
0	0	0	0	0	0	0
0.6	0.7	0.7	0.6	0.6	0.6	0.7
3.8	3.9	4.0	4.1	4.1	4.2	3.7
0	0	0	–	–	–	0
4.1	3.5	3.2	–	–	–	3.2

Table 2-15: Effect of Choice of Geometry on Energies of Bond Separation

Bond Separation Reaction	HF/6-31G*//			SVWN/6-31G*//		
	AM1	3-21G$^{(*)}$	6-31G*	AM1	3-21G$^{(*)}$	SVWN/6-31G*
$CH_3CH_2CH_3 + CH_4 \rightarrow 2CH_3CH_3$	1	1	1	3	3	2
$CH(CH_3)_3 + 2CH_4 \rightarrow 3CH_3CH_3$	3	2	2	8	8	6
$C(CH_3)_4 + 3CH_4 \rightarrow 4CH_3CH_3$	5	3	3	14	13	11
$SiH_2(CH_3)_2 + SiH_4 \rightarrow 2CH_3SiH_3$	0	0	0	1	1	0
$SiH(CH_3)_3 + 2SiH_4 \rightarrow 3CH_3SiH_3$	1	0	1	2	2	1
$Si(CH_3)_4 + 3SiH_4 \rightarrow 4CH_3SiH_3$	3	0	1	5	3	1
$CH_3CH_2NH_2 + CH_4 \rightarrow CH_3CH_3 + CH_3NH_2$	3	3	3	6	6	5
$CH_3NHCH_3 + NH_3 \rightarrow 2CH_3NH_2$	3	2	2	4	4	4
$(CH_3)_3N + 2NH_3 \rightarrow 3CH_3NH_2$	6	5	5	11	10	11
$CH_3CH_2OH + CH_4 \rightarrow CH_3CH_3 + CH_3OH$	5	4	4	7	7	6
$CH_3OCH_3 + H_2O \rightarrow 2CH_3OH$	3	3	3	4	4	5
$CH_3CH_2SH + CH_4 \rightarrow CH_3CH_3 + CH_3SH$	1	1	1	4	3	3
$CH_3SCH_3 + H_2S \rightarrow 2CH_3SH$	2	1	1	3	2	2
$CH_2F_2 + CH_4 \rightarrow 2CH_3F$	12	14	14	17	19	18
$CHF_3 + 2CH_4 \rightarrow 3CH_3F$	32	37	36	44	50	47
$CF_4 + 3CH_4 \rightarrow 4CH_3F$	53	59	58	73	80	75
$CH_2Cl_2 + CH_4 \rightarrow 2CH_3Cl$	−3	−4	−4	1	2	1
$CHCl_3 + 2CH_4 \rightarrow 3CH_3Cl$	−10	−12	−12	1	2	0
$CCl_4 + 3CH_4 \rightarrow 4CH_3Cl$	−23	−26	−29	−2	−2	−5
$CH_3CHCH_2 + CH_4 \rightarrow CH_3CH_3 + CH_2CH_2$	4	4	4	7	7	7
$CH_3CHO + CH_4 \rightarrow CH_3CH_3 + H_2CO$	10	10	10	14	14	13
$CH_3CCH + CH_4 \rightarrow CH_3CH_3 + HCCH$	7	8	8	12	12	12
$CH_3CN + CH_4 \rightarrow CH_3CH_3 + HCN$	11	12	12	15	15	13
$CH_2CCH_2 + CH_4 \rightarrow 2CH_2CH_2$	−5	−5	−4	5	5	5

Reactions

B3LYP/6-31G*//			MP2/6-31G*//			
AM1	3-21G(*)	B3LYP/ 6-31G*	AM1	3-21G(*)	MP2/ 6-31G*	expt.
2	1	1	3	2	2	2.6
5	4	3	7	6	6	7.5
7	6	4	13	11	11	13.1
1	0	0	1	0	0	0.4
2	0	0	3	1	1	1.6
3	1	0	5	2	2	2.8
4	4	4	5	4	4	2.9
6	2	3	5	4	4	3.8
7	6	7	12	11	11	9.5
6	5	5	6	5	5	5.0
3	3	3	5	5	5	4.4
2	2	2	3	3	3	2.7
2	1	2	3	3	3	2.2
14	15	15	15	16	16	13.3
37	39	38	39	41	41	32.9
60	62	60	64	65	64	49.3
0	−1	−1	0	0	0	0.9
−4	−5	−6	−1	−2	−3	−0.1
−11	−14	−16	−6	−7	—	−1.8
5	6	5	5	5	5	4.7
12	12	11	11	11	11	10.7
10	10	10	7	8	8	7.2
13	13	13	11	11	11	14.4
1	1	1	−3	−2	−2	−3.9

Table 2-15: Effect of Choice of Geometry on Energies of Bond Separation

Bond Separation Reaction	HF/6-31G*//			SVWN/6-31G*//		
	AM1	3-21G$^{(*)}$	6-31G*	AM1	3-21G$^{(*)}$	SVWN/6-31G*
$CH_2CO + CH_4 \rightarrow CH_2CH_2 + H_2CO$	12	14	14	24	25	24
$CO_2 + CH_4 \rightarrow 2H_2CO$	58	62	61	69	70	68
$CH_2CHCHCH_2 + 2CH_4 \rightarrow CH_3CH_3 + 2CH_2CH_2$	11	11	11	19	20	18
$NH_2CHO + CH_4 \rightarrow CH_3NH_2 + H_2CO$	31	32	31	40	41	39
$+ 6CH_4 \rightarrow 3CH_3CH_3 + 3CH_2CH_2$	60	58	58	75	77	73
$+ 5CH_4 + NH_3 \rightarrow 2CH_3CH_3 + 2CH_2CH_2 + CH_3NH_2 + CH_2NH$	62	61	61	78	82	75
$+ 4CH_4 + 2NH_3 \rightarrow 2CH_3CH_3 + CH_2CH_2 + 2CH_2NH + NH_2NH_2$	57	52	54	74	77	68
$+ 4CH_4 + 2NH_3 \rightarrow CH_3CH_3 + CH_2CH_2 + 2CH_3NH_2 + 2CH_2NH$	66	66	66	80	88	78
$+ 4CH_4 + 2NH_3 \rightarrow CH_3CH_3 + CH_2CH_2 + 2CH_3NH_2 + 2CH_2NH$	60	59	60	76	84	75
$+ 3CH_4 \rightarrow 3CH_3CH_3$	−24	−26	−26	−28	−29	−30
$+ 2CH_4 + NH_3 \rightarrow CH_3CH_3 + 2CH_3NH_2$	−21	−23	−22	−25	−25	−26
$+ 2CH_4 + H_2O \rightarrow CH_3CH_3 + 2CH_3OH$	−19	−21	−22	−21	−22	−22
$+ 2CH_4 + H_2S \rightarrow CH_3CH_3 + 2CH_3SH$	−13	−16	−16	−16	−17	−18

Reactions (continued)

B3LYP/6-31G*//			MP2/6-31G*//			
AM1	3-21G(*)	B3LYP/6-31G*	AM1	3-21G(*)	MP2/6-31G*	expt.
18	19	18	16	17	17	15.0
61	62	62	65	65	66	60.9
16	16	15	15	14	14	11.3
34	35	34	33	34	33	29.8
70	69	67	73	72	71	64.2
70	72	68	76	75	74	71.9
68	62	62	74	69	69	74.6
75	73	72	81	79	78	80.4
71	69	68	76	75	75	80.5
−23	−25	−25	−22	−24	−24	−22.1
−19	−20	−21	−17	−18	−18	−17.4
−17	−17	−17	−13	−14	−13	−13.7
−10	−13	−13	−8	−11	−11	−14.9

Table 2-15: Effect of Choice of Geometry on Energies of Bond Separation

Bond Separation Reaction	HF/6-31G*//			SVWN/6-31G*//		
	AM1	3-21G(*)	6-31G*	AM1	3-21G(*)	SVWN/6-31G*
(structure) + $4CH_4 \rightarrow 4CH_3CH_3$	−21	−24	−24	−22	−23	−24
(structure) + $3CH_4 \rightarrow 2CH_3CH_3 + CH_2CH_2$	−50	−51	−51	−49	−49	−51
(structure) + $4CH_4 \rightarrow 3CH_3CH_3 + CH_2CH_2$	−22	−24	−24	−19	−19	−20
(structure) + $5CH_4 \rightarrow 3CH_3CH_3 + 2CH_2CH_2$	12	11	11	23	24	22
(structure) + $4CH_4 + H_2S \rightarrow CH_3CH_3 + 2CH_3SH + 2CH_2CH_2$	29	29	29	45	47	46
(structure) + $4CH_4 \rightarrow 3CH_3CH_3 + CH_2CH_2$	−29	−31	−31	−26	−26	−29
(structure) + $6CH_4 \rightarrow 5CH_3CH_3$	−62	−64	−63	−66	−64	−67

Reactions (continued)

B3LYP/6-31G*//			MP2/6-31G*//			
AM1	3-21G[(*)]	B3LYP/ 6-31G*	AM1	3-21G[(*)]	MP2/ 6-31G*	expt.
−19	−21	−22	−19	−20	−19	−15.9
−45	−45	−46	−44	−45	−45	−43.9
−17	−19	−20	−17	−19	−18	−17.3
21	19	17	22	22	21	22.4
40	38	38	43	46	46	29.2
−23	−25	−27	−25	−25	−27	−24.5
−55	−57	−59	−55	−56	−55	−51.5

Table 2-16: Effect of Choice of Geometry on Proton Affinities Relative to Ammonia[a]

nitrogen base	HF/6-31G*//		SVWN/6-31G*//			B3LYP/6-31G*//			MP2/6-31G*//			expt.
	AM1	6-31G*	AM1	6-31G*	SVWN/6-31G*	AM1	6-31G*	B3LYP/6-31G*	AM1	6-31G*	MP2/6-31G*	
nitrogen	-100	-99	-97	-96	-95	-97	-96	-96	-98	-98	-98	-94
acetonitrile	-25	-23	-25	-24	-23	-24	-23	-23	-29	-28	-29	-17
methyleneimine	5	5	-3	-2	-2	-1	0	1	-2	-1	-1	-3
ammonia	0	0	0	0	0	0	0	0	0	0	0	0
aniline	7	8	-1	0	0	3	5	6	4	5	5	7
methylamine	9	11	7	8	8	8	10	10	9	10	10	9
aziridine	13	14	6	7	8	9	11	11	8	10	9	10
ethylamine	13	14	10	10	11	11	13	13	11	12	13	12
pyridine	16	18	10	13	13	14	16	16	11	13	13	15
dimethylamine	15	18	11	12	13	13	16	16	14	16	16	16
trimethylamine	19	22	12	14	14	16	19	19	17	20	19	19
quinuclidine	30	33	22	26	25	26	30	30	—	—	—	30

a) Energies (enthalpies) of reactions: $BH^+ + NH_3 \rightarrow B + NH_4^+$

Table 2-17: Effect of Choice of Geometry on Relative Energies of Products of Diels Alder Cycloadditions of Substituted Cyclopentadienes with Acrylonitrile

substituent on cyclopentadiene	HF/6-31G*//			SVWN/6-31G*//			B3LYP/6-31G*//		
	AM1	3-21G(*)	6-31G*	AM1	3-21G(*)	SVWN/ 6-31G*	AM1	3-21G(*)	B3LYP/ 6-31G*
1-methyl	0.1 (o)	0.2 (o)	0.2 (o)	0.3 (o)	0.0	0.6 (o)	0.2 (o)	0.0	0.2 (m)
1-methoxy	0.9 (m)	0.4 (m	0.5 (m)	0.1 (m)	0.1 (m)	1.0 (o)	0.7 (m)	0.6 (m)	0.1 (o)
2-methyl	0.1 (p)	0.2 (p)	0.1 (p)	0.8 (m)	1.2 (m)	1.0 (m)	0.2 (m)	0.3 (m)	0.2 (m)
2-methoxy	1.3 (p)	1.3 (p)	1.2 (p)	0.2 (p)	0.1 (p)	0.6 (p)	0.5 (p)	0.6 (p)	0.8 (p)
5-methyl	0.6 (a)	0.5 (a)	0.6 (a)	0.2 (s)	0.5 (s)	0.5 (s)	0.5 (a)	0.2 (a)	0.4 (a)
5-methoxy	4.6 (s)	4.4 (s)	4.5 (s)	4.6 (s)	4.8 (s)	5.0 (s)	4.1 (s)	3.9 (s)	4.2 (s)
5-trimethylsilyl	0.1 (a)	2.3 (a)	2.6 (a)	1.1 (s)	1.9 (a)	0.8 (a)	0.4 (s)	2.6 (a)	2.3 (a)
5-chloro	2.6 (s)	2.8 (s)	2.8 (s)	3.7 (s)	3.8 (s)	4.3 (s)	2.8 (s)	2.9 (s)	3.1 (s)

a) o = *ortho* product; p = *para* product; m = *meta* product; s = *syn* product; a = *anti* product.

B3LYP) and MP2 methods with the 6-31+G* basis set, which includes a single set of diffuse s- and p-type functions on all heavy atoms. The two sets of structures have been considered for each method (eight different sets of structures in all); structures using the underlying 6-31G* basis set as well as those obtained using the 6-31+G* basis set. Experimental data have been included to allow assessment of the errors incurred as a result of use of approximate geometries, relative to errors inherent to the methods in describing relative acidity.

The data clearly show that choice of structure is of little consequence. The conclusion is that it is probably not worth the additional effort to use basis sets with supplementary diffuse functions for the purpose of structure determination in anionic systems.

2.11   Are there molecules for which equilibrium geometries from semi-empirical and/or low-level *ab initio* methods are sufficiently poor to cause unacceptable errors in thermochemical comparisons?

The answer to this question is obviously "yes", but it is very difficult to generalize. For example, we have already pointed out (**Section 2.9**) the known flaw in HF/3-21G calculations with regard to the local geometry about nitrogen in amines, but the same level of calculation provides a generally credible account of bond angles involving other first-row elements and of bond angles in phosphorous compounds. Semi-empirical models behave similarly. While they generally provide descriptions of equilibrium geometries which are adequate for energy and other property comparisons, there are cases where calculated structures are very poor.

The best (and only) advice which can be given in operating in areas where there is little or no prior experience, is to test any proposed strategy on related systems for which experimental data are available, or where experimental data are unavailable, to perform higher-level calculations. Comparison of theory and experiment should not be the primary objective of computational investigations, although calibration of methods and strategies is necessary in advance of original applications.

We have also previously commented (**Section 2.8**) that infrequently "limiting" Hartree-Fock geometries differ significantly from structures obtained from MP2 correlated or density functional models using the same basis sets. For example, bonds involving two highly-electronegative elements, e.g., the OO bond in hydrogen peroxide, are poorly described at the Hartree-Fock limit and well described using correlated techniques. On the other hand, the structures of many hypervalent compunds are poorly reproduced using the MP2 model or one or more of the common density functional models, whereas Hartree-Fock schemes provide good descriptions. In these cases, use of Hartree-Fock models to provide geometries for energy calculations at correlated levels may lead to unacceptable errors.

Table 2-18: Effect of Choice of Geometry on Acidities of Carbon Acids Relative to Methane

acid XCH$_3$	HF/6-31+G*//		SVWN/6-31+G//		B3LYP/6-31+G*//		MP2/6-31+G*//		expt.
	6-31G*	6-31+G*	6-31G*	6-31+G*	6-31G*	6-31+G*	6-31G*	6-31+G*	
propene	28	26	34	32	31	29	30	28	26
toluene	33	31	42	40	37	36	36	34	38
1,1,1-trifluoroethane	32	31	36	34	36	34	37	35	42 ± 3
acetonitrile	47	45	52	50	49	47	47	45	44
acetaldehyde	53	52	59	57	56	54	57	55	50
nitromethane	68	66	69	68	68	67	67	65	58

a) Energies (enthalpies) of reactions: X–CH$_2^-$ + CH$_4$ → X–CH$_3$ + CH$_3^-$.

2.12 Are there properties which are particularly sensitive to choice of equilibrium geometry or which require "exact" equilibrium geometry in order to be properly evaluated?

The fact that energies of chemical reactions generally do not show large variations with choice of equilibrium structure suggests that errors in structure are systematic, and that we are benefiting from cancellation (see **Section 2.9**). Absolute energies are, of course, much more sensitive to choice of geometry, as would be the energies of reactions leading to atoms, e.g., homolytic bond dissociation energies. Some other properties also show strong dependence on geometry, perhaps most important among them, electric dipole moments. For example, the data in **Table 2-19** show that the electric dipole moments in a variety of nitrogen, oxygen, silicon, phosphorous and sulfur containing compounds are quite sensitive to exact choice of equilibrium geometry. This conclusion holds not only for calculations at the HF/6-31G* level, but also for density functional (SVWN/6-31G* and B3LYP/6-31G*) and for correlated MP2/6-31G* calculations. In these cases, the changes in electric dipole moment arise mainly because of significant variations in bond angle about the heteroatom center, the extent of which for ammonia and trimethylamine is illustrated in **Table 2-20**. On the other hand, calculated dipole moments for other classes of compounds, e.g., hydrocarbons (**Table 2-21**), show very little sensitivity to the level of calculation used to obtain geometry. The user should exercise caution in utilizing approximate geometries for dipole moment calculations, and precede investigations of "new" systems with sufficient calibration studies.

Figure 2-25 provides graphical display of changes in dipole moments resulting from changes in underlying geometry for Hartree-Fock models only. Specifically what is plotted are 6-31G*//AM1 and 6-31G*//3-21G[*] dipole moments vs. "exact" values (6-31G*//6-31G*). Similar plots, leading to similar conclusions, could be made for SVWN, B3LYP and MP2 calculations.

The same advice applies here as already provided in the previous sections. In the absence of prior experience, perform sufficient calculations to judge the sensitivity of property to choice of geometry. Only then can confidence be established in a particular choice of model.

"Exact" equilibrium structures **must be used** for the calculation of vibrational frequencies and associated normal vibration modes, as well as thermodynamic properties such as entropies obtained from calculated frequencies. This is because the energy second derivatives (in terms of coordinate displacements) are part of a Taylor series,

$$E = E^\circ + E' + E'' + \ldots ,$$

where E° is a constant, and E' (the first derivative term) is assumed to be rigorously zero. (Higher-order terms are also generally ignored.) Frequencies evaluated at non-equilibrium structures are meaningless!

2.13 Is it always necessary to optimize structures in the presence of solvent, or may gas-phase geometries be employed instead?

Methods now exist to account for the presence of solvent on the structures, energies and other properties of isolated (gas-phase) molecules. Among the more practical, are parameterized schemes which model the solvent in terms of a static electric field. These include the AM1-SM2 Model of Cramer and Truhlar[12] and the $AM1_{aq}$ model of Dixon, Leonard and Hehre,[13] both of which are parameterized to account for water as a solvent and are based on the AM1 semi-empirical model.[14] While both the AM1-SM2 and $AM1_{aq}$ models are only slightly more costly computationally than the underlying AM1 method for single energy (property) calculations, at the present time they are significantly (one or two orders of magnitude) more expensive for geometry optimization. It is of interest then to see what effect if any inclusion of solvent has on equilibrium geometry.

Table 2-22 shows heavy-atom bond distances in a few simple neutral molecules obtained using the AM1 (gas phase) and AM1-SM2 and $AM1_{aq}$ (aqueous) models. Note, that bond length changes from the gas phase are very small for both models for all molecules considered. The corresponding energy lowerings (resulting from using proper solvated structures in lieu of gas-phase structures) are also tiny. It is clear that in these cases optimization in the presence of solvent is not of significant benefit.

The situation is a little less clear in dealing with charged species. The data in **Table 2-23** compares heavy-atom bond lengths in a few ions obtained from AM1 and AM1-SM2 calculations, along with energy lowerings resulting from use of "aqueous" rather than gas-phase geometries. (The $AM1_{aq}$ model is not presently available for ions.) First, note that the effects are much larger than those previously noted for neutral molecules; bond distances typically alter by 0.02 - 0.03 Å, and energies are lowered by approximately 1 kcal/mol. Note also, that the bond length changes are in the anticipated direction: solvent would be expected to lead to increased polarity[15] as evidenced by an increase in the lengths of bonds to atoms bearing the charge.

Geometry optimization in the presence of solvent may well be advisable for ions, although a strong case cannot be made one way or the other. In this regard, it should be noted that the energy lowerings seen here for simple ions (~ 1 kcal/mol) would not be expected to increase dramatically (if at all) for large systems, as structural deformations should largely be confined to local charged regions.

Some warnings need to be provided. For one, solvation sometimes leads to a change in tautomeric form. The extreme cases are amino acids. For example, while in the gas phase glycine is most stable as an "uncharged" molecule, i.e., $H_2NCH_2CO_2H$, in water it prefers a zwitterionic structure, i.e.,

---

12. C.J. Cramer and D.G. Truhlar, J.Am. Chem. Soc., **113**, 8305 (1991); (b) C.J. Cramer and D.G. Truhlar, Science, **256**, 213 (1992); (c) C.J. Cramer and D.G. Truhlar, J. Comp. Aid. Mol. Des., **6**, 69 (1992)
13. R.W. Dixon, J. M. Leonard and W.J. Hehre, Israel J. Chem., **33**, 427 (1993).
14. Solvation models have also been developed to be used in conjugation with MNDO and PM3 semi-empirical methods and as well with *ab initio* methods. They lead to broadly similar conclusions regarding structure as the AM1 based schemes addressed here.
15. Electric dipole moments for molecules in solution are typically larger than gas-phase dipole moments.

Table 2-19: **Effect of Choice of Geometry on Electric Dipole Moments in**

heteroatom	molecule	HF/6-31G*//			SVWN/6-31G*//		
		AM1	3-21G[(*)]	6-31G*	AM1	3-21G[(*)]	SVWN/6-31G*
Nitrogen	Me_3N	0.64	0.73	0.75	0.40	0.50	0.47
	Me_2NH	1.05	1.02	1.14	0.92	0.89	0.97
	$EtNH_2$	1.44	1.26	1.49	1.33	1.16	1.45
	$MeNH_2$	1.42	1.30	1.53	1.35	1.22	1.44
	NH_3	1.80	1.55	1.92	1.79	1.54	1.97
	$PhNH_2$	1.54	1.60	1.54	1.86	2.10	2.00
	▷NH (aziridine)	1.83	2.01	1.94	1.62	1.76	1.74
	⬡N (pyridine)	2.35	2.31	2.31	2.20	2.16	2.19
Oxygen	Me_2O	1.54	1.64	1.48	1.18	1.30	1.16
	$EtOH$	1.78	1.80	1.74	1.53	1.54	1.50
	$MeOH$	1.90	1.95	1.87	1.67	1.71	1.65
	H_2O	2.25	2.18	2.20	2.15	2.08	2.15
	▷O (oxirane)	2.35	2.64	2.28	1.79	2.03	1.80
Silicon	Me_3SiH	0.64	0.51	0.51	0.77	0.67	0.74
	$MeSiH_3$	0.81	0.69	0.68	0.99	0.86	0.96
	Me_2SiH_2	0.83	0.68	0.67	1.01	0.87	0.97
	$EtSiH_3$	0.85	0.77	0.75	1.02	0.93	1.00
Phosphorous	PH_3	0.99	0.87	0.88	1.32	1.25	1.15
	$MePH_2$	1.43	1.27	1.27	1.70	1.57	1.50
	$EtPH_2$	1.59	1.37	1.32	1.76	1.61	1.54
	Me_3P	1.46	1.37	1.37	1.52	1.54	1.47
	Me_2PH	1.51	1.37	1.37	1.69	1.62	1.55
Sulfur	⬠S (thiophene)	0.68	0.89	0.90	0.49	0.62	0.55
	H_2S	1.42	1.41	1.41	1.61	1.60	1.57
	Me_2S	1.67	1.81	1.80	1.70	1.82	1.76
	$MeSH$	1.71	1.79	1.79	1.80	1.86	1.80
	$EtSH$	1.74	1.85	1.86	1.79	1.87	1.83
	▷S (thiirane)	2.14	2.31	2.31	1.99	2.09	2.07

Molecules Containing Heteroatoms

B3LYP/6-31G*//			MP2/6-31G*//			
AM1	3-21G$^{(*)}$	MP2/ 6-31G*	AM1	3-21G$^{(*)}$	MP2/	expt.
0.45	0.55	0.58	0.54	0.64	0.74	0.61
0.91	0.89	1.03	0.99	0.97	1.16	1.03
1.31	1.14	1.44	1.39	1.22	1.54	1.22
1.32	1.20	1.47	1.40	1.27	1.57	1.31
1.73	1.49	1.91	1.80	1.55	1.97	1.47
1.72	1.93	1.72	1.64	1.80	1.63	1.53
1.62	1.76	1.78	1.72	1.87	1.90	1.90
2.19	2.15	2.19	2.30	2.26	2.32	2.19
1.25	1.35	1.28	1.37	1.47	1.44	1.30
1.55	1.56	1.56	1.66	1.67	1.68	1.69
1.67	1.71	1.69	1.80	1.83	1.84	1.70
2.09	2.03	2.10	2.20	2.14	2.20	1.85
1.89	2.14	1.95	2.01	2.24	2.11	1.89
0.70	0.59	0.62	0.68	0.56	0.57	0.53
0.90	0.79	0.82	0.86	0.73	0.74	0.74
0.92	0.79	0.82	0.88	0.73	0.74	0.75
0.93	0.86	0.87	0.90	0.80	0.80	0.81
1.13	1.04	0.96	1.12	1.03	1.00	0.58
1.54	1.39	1.32	1.52	1.37	1.33	1.10
1.63	1.45	1.38	1.65	1.44	1.40	1.17
1.43	1.41	1.35	1.49	1.44	1.41	1.19
1.57	1.46	1.39	1.58	1.45	1.42	1.23
0.50	0.66	0.63	0.46	0.63	0.53	0.55
1.46	1.45	1.43	1.50	1.49	1.48	0.97
1.62	1.75	1.72	1.67	1.79	1.75	1.50
1.70	1.76	1.74	1.72	1.78	1.75	1.52
1.70	1.80	1.80	1.73	1.81	1.78	1.58
1.97	2.10	2.15	1.99	2.10	2.10	1.85

Table 2-20: HNH Bond Angle in Ammonia and CNC Bond Angle in Trimethylamine as a Function of Theoretical Model

model	NH_3	NMe_3
AM1	105.2	113.0
HF/3-21G	112.4	113.1
HF/6-31G*	107.2	111.9
SVWN/6-31G*	106.1	110.7
B3LYP/6-31G*	105.7	111.5
MP2/6-31G*	106.3	110.4
expt.	106.7	110.9

$^+H_3NCH_2CO_2^-$. Many less dramatic examples exist, in particular, with hetero-cylic compounds. Where multiple tautomers exist, it will at the very least be necessary to examine the role of solvent in altering relative gas-phase energies; full optimization of the individual tautomer geometries may then be necessary to reproduce subtle differences in their energies, in particular where ions are involved.[16]

Solvation is also known to effect changes in conformation. For example, polypeptides in the gas phase would be expected to adopt "linear" (stretched out) structures as opposed to compact (globular) structures found in solution (and naturally for proteins). Again, less dramatic systems are common. We will address this topic further in **Section 6.7**.

---

16. Future versions of *SPARTAN* will provide for automatic searching of tautomers.

Table 2-21: Effect of Choice of Geometry on Electric Dipole Moments in

formula	molecule	HF/6-31G*//			SVWN/6-31G*//		
		AM1	3-21G[(*)]	6-31G*	AM1	3-21G[(*)]	6-31G*
C_3H_4	propyne	0.58	0.64	0.64	0.75	0.78	0.77
	cyclopropene	0.54	0.54	0.56	0.49	0.49	0.52
C_3H_6	propene	0.29	0.30	0.31	0.41	0.40	0.43
C_3H_8	propane	0.07	0.07	0.07	0.07	0.05	0.05
C_4H_4	but-1-yne-3-ene	0.43	0.48	0.47	0.29	0.34	0.35
C_4H_6	cyclobutene	0.01	0.04	0.03	0.19	0.19	0.21
	1,2-butadiene	0.32	0.36	0.36	0.42	0.43	0.44
	1-butyne	0.56	0.65	0.65	0.69	0.74	0.72
	methylenecyclopropane	0.39	0.38	0.40	0.45	0.44	0.47
	bicyclo[1.1.0] butane	0.62	0.67	0.75	0.61	0.68	0.83
	1-methylcyclopropene	0.85	0.88	0.89	0.94	0.94	0.96
C_4H_8	isobutene	0.43	0.45	0.45	0.56	0.57	0.61
	cis-2-butene	0.10	0.13	0.14	0.17	0.18	0.21
	cis-1-butene	0.33	0.35	0.36	0.46	0.46	0.49
	methylcyclopropane	0.09	0.11	0.10	0.11	0.13	0.11
C_4H_{10}	isobutane	0.10	0.10	0.10	0.10	0.09	0.08

Hydrocarbons

B3LYP/6-31G*//			MP2/6-31G*//			
AM1	3-21G[(*)]	6-31G*	AM1	3-21G[(*)]	6-31G*	expt.
0.64	0.69	0.69	0.55	0.60	0.61	0.75
0.52	0.50	0.52	0.50	0.50	0.50	0.45
0.34	0.34	0.36	0.27	0.27	0.28	0.36
0.06	0.05	0.05	0.06	0.05	0.05	0.08
0.31	0.37	0.33	0.26	0.32	0.30	0.4
0.08	0.11	0.11	0.07	0.09	0.10	0.13
0.38	0.40	0.41	0.29	0.32	0.32	0.40
0.61	0.68	0.68	0.51	0.59	0.59	0.80
0.40	0.39	0.41	0.32	0.31	0.2	0.40
0.61	0.66	0.77	0.61	0.68	0.82	0.68
0.89	0.90	0.91	0.81	0.84	0.83	0.84
0.48	0.50	0.50	0.37	0.40	0.40	0.50
0.15	0.16	0.18	0.13	0.14	0.16	0.26
0.38	0.40	0.41	0.30	0.31	0.33	0.44
0.10	0.11	0.11	0.09	0.11	0.10	0.14
0.09	0.08	0.08	0.09	0.08	0.08	0.13

Figure 2-25: Electric Dipole Moments as a Function of Changes in Geometry. □=6-31G*//AM1 vs. 6-31G*//6-31G*, ○=6-31G*/3-21G⁽*⁾ vs. 6-31G//6-31G*.

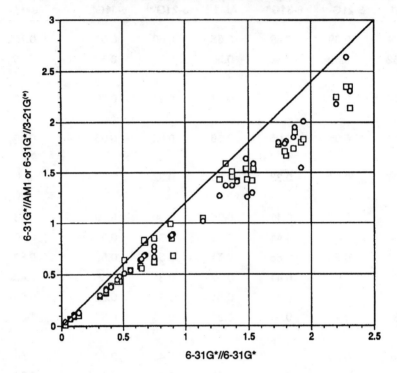

Table 2-22: **AM1, AM1-SM2 and AM1$_{aq}$ Equilibrium Bond Distances and Energy Lowerings Relative to AM1 in Neutral Molecules**

molecule	AM1	AM1-SM2		AM1$_{aq}$	
		distance	ΔE	distance	ΔE
(pyridine structure)	1.347	1.347	0.4	1.347	0.2
	1.407	1.407		1.407	
	1.396	1.396		1.396	
(piperazine structure)	1.450	1.448	0.1	1.444	0.5
	1.542	1.542		1.543	
(acetic acid structure)	1.486	1.488	0.1	1.455	0.0
	1.234	1.243		1.236	
	1.364	1.362		1.362	
(tetrahydrofuran structure)	1.430	1.433	0.0	1.429	0.0
	1.525	1.524		1.525	
	1.523	1.522		1.523	
(vinyl chloride structure)	1.696	1.704	0.0	1.703	0.0
	1.329	1.328		1.328	

Table 2-23: AM1 and AM1-SM2 Equilibrium Bond Distances and Energy Lowerings Relative to AM1 in Ions.

molecule	AM1	AM1-SM2	
		distance	ΔE
	1.267	1.289	0.9
	1.528	1.512	
	1.310	1.347	1.1
	1.488	1.486	0.7

3

Obtaining Transition Structures and Verifying Reaction Pathways

Chemists are familiar with description of a chemical reaction in terms of the simple "one dimensional" potential energy diagram.

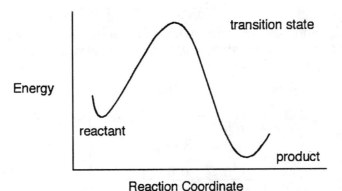

This describes the overall process in terms of a continuous motion along the reaction coordinate from reactant to product through the transition state. The central idea, now known as **transition state theory**, is that the height of the barrier separating reactant from product relates directly to the overall rate of reaction.

In fact, the simple reaction coordinate diagram above tells us more than just about reaction rate ("kinetics"). The positions of the minima along the reaction coordinate give us directly the equilibrium geometries of reactant and product. The position of the maximum tells us about the geometry of the transition state, which of course we cannot measure. Finally, the relative energies of reactant and product relate directly to abundance of these species at infinite time ("thermodynamics").

It is useful at this point to characterize mathematically the reaction coordinate diagram above, and in so doing the situation in the general multi-dimensional case. Reactant, product and transition state are all stationary points on the potential energy surface. In one dimension this means that at these points the (total) derivative of the energy with respect to the reaction coordinate (R) is zero,

$$\frac{dE}{dR} = 0 \ .$$

The same is true in many dimensions (generally 3N-6 dimensions for a system comprising N atoms), where the partial derivatives of the energy with respect to each of the 3N-6 independent coordinates (R_i) is zero,

$$\frac{\partial E}{\partial R_i} = 0 \ .$$

In the one-dimenisonal case, minima are points for which the second derivative of the energy with regard to the geometrical coordinate are greater than zero,

$$\frac{d^2E}{dR^2} > 0 \ ,$$

and transition states (maxima) are points for which the second derivative are less than zero,

$$\frac{d^2E}{dR^2} < 0 \ .$$

In many dimensions the situation is more complicated, because the single second derivative is now a matrix of partial second derivatives.

$$\begin{pmatrix} \dfrac{\partial^2E}{\partial R_1^2} & \dfrac{\partial^2E}{\partial R_1 \partial R_2} & \cdots & \\[2em] \dfrac{\partial^2E}{\partial R_2 \partial R_1} & \dfrac{\partial^2E}{\partial R_2^2} & & \\[2em] \vdots & & \ddots & \dfrac{\partial^2E}{\partial R_{3N-6}^2} \end{pmatrix}$$

The solution is to find an alternative set of geometrical coordinates (ξ_i) for which the matrix of second derivatives is now diagonal, i.e.,

$$
\begin{pmatrix}
\dfrac{\partial^2 E}{\partial \xi_1^2} & & & 0 \\[2ex]
& \dfrac{\partial^2 E}{\partial \xi_2^2} & & \\[2ex]
& & \ddots & \dfrac{\partial^2 E}{\partial \xi_{3N-6}^2} \\[2ex]
0 & & &
\end{pmatrix}
$$

The ξ_i are referred to as **normal coordinates**. Within this new coordinate system, minima are characterized by all postive second derivatives,

$$
\frac{\partial^2 E}{\partial \xi_i^2} > 0 \quad i=1,2,\ldots 3N-6,
$$

and transistion states are characterized by all positive second derivatives except for one corresponding to the reaction coordinate (ξ_p) for which the second derivative is negative,

$$
\frac{\partial^2 E}{\partial \xi_p} < 0 .
$$

One can think of this situation as having split the many dimensional problem into two parts, thereby allowing its consideration with no more difficulty than the simple one-dimensional case.

    Whereas the reactant, the product and the transition state are all well defined as stationary points on the overall potential energy surface, the reaction coordinate which smoothly connects them, is not. For simple reactions, such as the unimolecular isomerism of hydrogen isocyanide to hydrogen cyanide, i.e.,

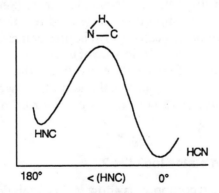

the reaction coordinate might be thought of in terms of a single geometrical coordinate, in this case the HNC bond angle. This angle is 180° in the reactant, 0° in the product and perhaps something slightly less than 90° in the transition state. It is easy to see, however, how rapidly the situation becomes complex. Consider, for example, the reaction coordinate describing the thermal elimination of ethylene from ethyl acetate.

$$
\underset{\substack{\text{CH}_3}}{\overset{\substack{\text{O}}}{H_2C \diagup \overset{}{\underset{\overset{}{\text{O}}}{C}}}}-\text{CH}_3 \longrightarrow \underset{\text{CH}_2}{\overset{\text{CH}_2}{\parallel}} + \underset{\text{OH}}{\overset{\text{O}}{C}}-\text{CH}_3
$$

In this case, no solitary bond distance change or bond angle change provides an adequate description. Some combination of motions is required, the exact nature of which is not at all obvious. Realize also that this still a very simple reaction, and the description of most other processes is likely to be even more involved.

In this chapter, we examine a number of issues related to determining and verifying transition states for chemical reactions. As in our previous treatment of equilibrium geometries (**Chapter 2**), we seek both to establish and evaluate practical strategies, and to point out ways in which overall computational effort can be reduced. Unlike the situation with equilibrium geometries, however, we do not have direct experimental evidence to back us up, and we need to rely almost entirely on the results of "high-quality" calculations to establish an overall level of confidence.

We start (**Section 3.1**) by asking what transition states look like, and then using this information go on (**Section 3.2**) to inquire why it is that finding transition states is more difficult (or at least perceived to be more difficult) than finding equilibrium structures. The next three sections address practical concerns: efficient methods for locating transition states (**Section 3.3**), ways to "guess" starting transition state geometries (**Section 3.4**) and verification of transition states (**Section 3.5**). The next two sections compare transition state geometries obtained at different levels of calculation (**Section 3.6**), and at the same level of calculation for functionally related reactions (**Section 3.7**). The first of the topics leads to discussion of whether transition state geometries obtained from low levels of calculation are of use obtaining activation energies using higher-level models. This is addressed in **Sections 3.8** and **Section 3.9**. **Section 3.10** discusses classes of chemical reactions for which transition states do not exist, and **Section 3.11** comments on the role of solvent in altering transition-state geometry.

3.1 What do transition states look like?

The structures of organic compounds show a very high degree of systematics. A short table of "average" bond distances, together with information about connectivity (a *valence structure*) is usually sufficient to accurately render a detailed geometry. This is, of course, why empirical schemes ("molecular mechanics") may be (and are) employed routinely to yield reasonable equilibrium geometries. The only caveat is conformation involving single bonds and/or flexible rings. Conformational energy differences may be quite small (a few kcal/mol compared with 50-100 kcal/mol for a typical bond energy), and it may be difficult to "guess" the most stable arrangement from among the many possibilities. Conformation remains the major difficulty in rendering accurate overall equilibrium structures. Further discussion is provided in **Chapter 6**.

The geometries of transition states on the pathway between reactants and products are, on the other hand, not as easily anticipated. This not to say that they do not exhibit systematics as do "normal" (stable) molecules, but rather that we do not yet have sufficient experience to identify what systematics, do exist, and more importantly how to capitalize on structural similarities. It needs to be recognized that transition states cannot even be detected let alone characterized experimentally, at least not directly. While measured activation energies relate to the energies of transition states above reactants, and while activation entropies and activation volumes as well as kinetic isotope effects may be invoked to imply some aspects of transition-state structure, no experiment can actually provide direct information about the detailed geometries and/or other physical properties of transition states. Quite simply, transition states do not exist in terms of a stable population of molecules on which experimental measurements may be made. Experimental activation parameters may act as a guide, although here too it needs to be pointed out that their interpretation is in terms of a theory (**transition state theory**), and even then, they tell little about what actually transpires in going from reactants to products.

In short, experiment alone cannot tell us what transition states "look like", at least with the detail we are accustomed to in dealing with equilibrium structures. On the other hand, quantum chemical calculations, at least *ab initio* calculations, do not (cannot) distinguish between systems which are stable and which may be scrutinized experimentally, and those which are labile (reactive intermediates) or do not even correspond to energy minima (transition states). The generality of the underlying theory, and (hopefully) the lack of intentional bias in formulating practical methods, ensures that structures, relative stabilities and other properties calculated for molecules for which experimental data are unavailable will be no poorer (and no better) than the same quantities obtained for stable molecules for which experimental data exist for comparison.

Quantum chemical methods which incorporate parameters (semi-empirical methods and some density functional methods) present some problems with regard to the description of transition states, for detailed parameterization is typically based on matching (experimental) data on stable structures. These problems can hopefully be resolved in the future with incorporation of data on transition states from high-level *ab initio* and/or non-parameterized correlated methods.

With experience we will be able to answer the question: "What do transition states look like?" No doubt calculations will uncover systematics in transition state geometries, just as experiment uncovered systematics in equilibrium structures. These observations will ultimately allow us to picture transition states as easily as we now view stable molecules.

3.2 Why is finding a transition structure more difficult than finding an equilibrium structure?

There are several reasons for this common perception, among the most important being:

i) The mathematical problem of finding a first-order saddle point (a transition state) is probably (but not necessarily) more difficult that that of finding a minimum. What is certainly true, is that techniques for locating transition states are much less well developed than procedures for finding minima (or maxima). After all, minimization is an important chore in many diverse fields of science and technology, whereas saddle point location has few if any important applications outside of chemistry.

Significant progress has been made in recent years in the development of methods and computer algorithms for location of transition states, and we can expect this progress to continue. In time, available techniques for transition state location should be of the same caliber as those now established for minima searching. Only then will we know if the mathematical problem is in fact more difficult.

ii) The "common wisdom" is that potential energy surfaces in the vicinity of transition states are more "flat" than surfaces in the vicinity of local minima. This is entirely reasonable; transition states represent a delicate balance of bond breaking and bond making, whereas overall bonding is maximized in equilibrium structures. The flatness of the potential energy surface complicates efforts to find transition states in two ways. For one, it suggests that the potential energy surface in the vicinity of a transition state may be less well described in terms of a simple quadratic function than the surface in the vicinity of a local minimum. All common optimization algorithms assume limiting quadratic behavior. The second consequence is that the geometries of transition states, even for closely related systems, or for the same system calculated at different levels of theory, might be expected to differ significantly. If true, this might limit the value of efforts to determine transition states for complex reactions based on structures for simpler processes and/or using lower levels of theory. (Further discussion is provided in **Sections 3.6** and **3.7**.)

There is a "silver lining". If the potential surface in the vicinity of the transition state is indeed flat, then large differences in transition-state structures should have little effect on calculated activation energies. Semi-empirical or low-level *ab initio* methods might very well provide suitable geometries for this purpose, even though their structural descriptions may differ significantly from those of higher-level models. (Further discussion is provided in **Sections 3.8** and **3.9**.)

iii) To the extent that transition states incorporate partially (or completely) broken bonds, it might be anticipated that low-level theoretical treatments will not provide satisfactory descriptions, and that models with large basis sets and accounting for electron correlation will be required. While this is certainly the case with regard to calculated absolute activation energies (see **Section 5.1**), it remains to be established to what extent extensions of basis set and/or electron correlation affect transition state geometry, or activation energy differences among closely related reactions (for additional discussion, see **Section 5.2**).

A related issue concerns the performance of parameterized semi-empirical models with regard to transition state geometries. Present generation semi-empirical schemes have been parameterized using experimental data on stable molecules, and would not be expected to perform as well in describing transition state structures as they would for equilibrium geometries. As such, they perhaps cannot be trusted to provide reasonable guess geometries. This is not to say that semi-empirical models will not perform well in those tasks, only that there is reason to be cautious. There is, of course, no reason why future generations of semi-empirical models could not be parameterized to reproduce transition-state geometries obtained from higher-level computational methods. (A similar concern applies to certain classes of density functional models which also incorporate parameters based on reproducing experimental equilibrium data.)

iv) We know relatively little about the geometries of transition states, at least by comparison with our extensive knowledge about the geometries of stable molecules. What we do know comes almost entirely from calculation. "Guessing" transition state geometries based on prior experience is therefore much more difficult than guessing equilibrium geometries. This predicament is obviously due in part to a complete lack of experimental structural data for transition states. It is also due to a lag in the application of computational methods to the study of transition states (and reaction mechanisms in general).

Overall the prognosis is very good. Optimization algorithms and computational models will continue to develop, as will our knowledge both about transition state geometries and about reaction mechanisms in general. Look for this to be one of the major areas for computation to impact practical chemistry.

3.3 What is the most efficient way to obtain a transition state geometry?

While, as pointed out earlier, the lack of experimental structure data on transition states makes it difficult to assess the performance of theoretical models, the same advice previously given for equilibrium structure determination (**Section 2.1**) generally applies here. Wherever possible, precede optimizations at high levels of theory by optimizations using semi-empirical or small basis set Hartree-Fock models, and/or on simplified model systems. Also recognize the value of a good Hessian (matrix of second energy derivatives) in addition to a good geometry at the start of an optimization. Semi-empirical methods will certainly be suitable for this task.

The effect of preceding *ab initio* transition state optimizations by semi-empirical optimizations on the number of optimization cycles required is illustrated in **Table 3-1** for a few simple organic reactions. Specifically, one set of 3-21G level optimizations has been carried out from "reasonable" starting geometries, while the other set uses AM1 geometries and Hessians. While it is unwise to generalize from such a small sample, it is clear that preliminary optimization using the AM1 model, followed by calculation of the Hessian at the AM1 level, effects reduction in total number of cycles required for optimization at the 3-21G level, sometimes significantly so. We want to emphasize that there is nothing special either about HF/3-21G as an optimization level or about AM1 as a means to supply guesses. We use these levels here only for illustration. The overall conclusion should carry over to other *ab initio* schemes (including density functional and correlated methods), and to other semi-empirical and low level *ab initio* models to supply the guess geometry and Hessian. Additional discussion on a closely-related topic will be provided in **Section 3.6**.

A word of warning: It needs to be recognized that present generation semi-empirical methods, sometimes give very poor descriptions of the geometries of reaction transition states. They have not been explicitly parameterized for this purpose. Also, some low-level Hartree-Fock models and density functional methods based on the local spin density approximation sometimes fail to produce reasonable transition state geometries. Some caution needs to be exercised in the use of these methods for this purpose.

Significant savings can also be achieved in some cases by preceding transition state optimization on the real system of interest by optimization on a closely-related model system. The idea here is that, even though transition state geometries vary somewhat from system to system, there may be a high degree of uniformity among closely-related systems. Additional discussion will be provided in **Section 3.7**. Operationally, what is required is to first perform a transition-state optimization on the model system, and then to modify the model to yield the real system without changing the local geometry around the reactive centers.[1] A new Hessian should be calculated (using semi-empirical methods).

The data in **Table 3-2** shows the effect of such a tactic on a few simple organic reactions for which models may easily be constructed. Here, calculations are at the semi-empirical AM1 level, although the conclusions should hold for other semi-empirical models, as well as for *ab initio* and correlated models. As before, while it is difficult to generalize from such a small data set, the value of preliminary semi-empirical calculations in reducing overall computation is clearly evident.

The overall recommendation is to use calculations from low-level methods, and/or closely related model systems wherever possible to furnish starting information for final transition state optimizations. While this adds a step to the overall optimization process,[2] the time savings which result are likely to be significant.

---

1. *SPARTAN* facilitates such a tactic by allowing optimization to be carried out subject to some atoms being "frozen".
2. As in the case of geometry optimization (see **Section 2.1**), *SPARTAN* allows such a two-step procedure to be carried out automatically, although because semi-empirical models sometimes produce unrealistic transition structures, it may be wise to inspect the intermediate results.

Table 3-1: Effect of Transition State Optimization and Hessian Calculation at the AM1 Level on the Number of Cycles Required for Transition State Optimization at the 3-21G Level

reaction	optimization cycles required	
	no guess	AM1 guess
Claisen rearrangement of methyl, vinyl ether	100	20
Diels-Alder cycloaddition of cyclopentadiene and acrylonitrile	98	45
pyrolysis of ethyl formate	165	87

Table 3-2: Effect of Transition State Optimization on "Model Reactions" on the Number of Cycles Required for Transition State Optimization on "Real Reactions"

real reaction	model reaction	optimization cycles required	
		no use of model	use of model
Diels-Alder cycloaddition of 5-chlorocyclopentadiene and acrylonitrile	Diels-Alder cycloaddition of cyclopentadiene and acrylonitrile	78	19
addition of singlet dichloro-carbene to cyclohexene	addition of singlet dichloro-carbene to ethylene	89	41
pyrolysis of cyclohexyl formate	pyrolysis of ethyl formate	291	191

3.4 What is the best way to get an initial guess at a transition state geometry?

This is not an easy question to answer in general terms, as investigations of different systems may require different overall strategies. Certainly there exist a number of reasonable alternative strategies. In order of the author's preference, these are:

i) Base the guess on the transition structure for a closely-related system which has previously been obtained at the same level of calculation, or alternatively on the transition structure for the same system obtained at a different (lower) level of theory. Where applicable, this strategy is clearly highly effective (see discussion in **Section 3.3**). In dealing with "new reactions", where there is no prior experience, the suggestion is to first gain experience with model systems and/or using low levels of calculation before finally proceeding with the systems or levels of calculation of actual interest.

In time, libraries of transition states for "common" chemical reactions will be compiled and made available.[3] These should greatly facilitate construction of transition states for derivative reactions, as well as practically guarantee success in finding transition states. Of course, in making use of such libraries, we are merely extending what chemists have done for many years with equilibrium geometries.

ii) Base the guess on an "average" of reactant and product geometries (**Linear Synchronous Transit** method).[4] This is straightforward for unimolecular reactions, but requires that separated product and/or reactant molecules in bimolecular (and higher-order reactions) be replaced by a "weak complex" on the way to product (reactant)[5]. Practical experience suggests that the most simple linear synchronous transit schemes are as effective as more involved recipes, where the contributions of reactant and product structures are weighed by thermochemical considerations (Hammond postulate).

iii) Base the guess on "chemical intuition", specifying critical bond lengths and angles in accord with preconceived notions of mechanism. If possible, do not impose symmetry on your structure guess, as this may limit its ability to alter in case your mechanistic assumption were to prove incorrect. Again, experience suggests that very few reactions actually maintain symmetry.

It may take several guesses to establish a transition state for a "new reaction". Don't be discouraged if you do not have success the first time.

---

3. Future versions of *SPARTAN* will incorporate libraries of transition state structures at several different "standard" levels of calculation.
4. See for example: T.A. Halgren and W.N. Lipscomb, Chem. Phys. Lett., 225 (1977).
5. One way to form such complexes is to maneuver CPK representations of the separated products (and/or reactants) such that they "touch". Complex formation is facilitated by the docking capabilities in *SPARTAN* as well as 3D viewing.

3.5 How can we be certain that a geometry corresponds to a reasonable transition structure?

There are two "tests" which need to be performed in order to verify that a given structure actually corresponds to a first-order saddle point (transition structure), and further that this saddle point smoothly connects potential energy minima corresponding to reactant and product:

i) Verify that the Hessian (matrix of second-energy derivatives with respect to coordinates) yields one and only one imaginary frequency. This requires that a normal-mode analysis be carried out on the proposed transition structure. This analysis must be carried out at the same level of calculation used to obtain the transition state, otherwise the results will be meaningless (see also **Section 2.12**). The imaginary frequency will typically be in the range of 400-2000 cm^{-1}, quite similar to real vibrational frequencies. In the case of flexible rotors, e.g., methyl groups, or "floppy rings", the analysis may yield one or more additional imaginary frequencies with very small (<100 cm^{-1}) values. These typically correspond to couplings of low energy modes and can usually be ignored; make certain that you verify what motions these small imaginary frequencies actually correspond to (see below) before doing so. Be wary of structures which yield only very small imaginary frequencies. This suggests a very low energy transition structure, which quite likely will not correspond to the particular reaction of interest. In this case, it will be necessary to start over with a new guess at the transition structure.

ii) Verify that the normal coordinate corresponding to the imaginary frequency smoothly connects reactants and products. A simple qualitative way to do this is to "animate" the normal coordinate corresponding to the imaginary frequency, that is, to "walk along" this coordinate without any additional optimization.[6] This offers the advantage of not requiring any further calculation (beyond the normal-mode analysis already performed), but has the disadvantage that such an animation will not lead to the precise reactant or to the precise product. This is because the normal coordinate is a fixed linear combination of geometrical motions which is appropriate only in the immediate vicinity of the transition state, and becomes less and less appropriate the further one moves away from the transition state. Even so, experience suggests that this tactic is a cheap and effective way to eliminate transition states which do not connect the reactant with the desired product. At the very least, it should be tried before more involved techniques (see below) are called upon.

Another (and much more costly) approach is to actually "follow" the reaction from transition state to both the reactant and (independently) the product. In practice, this involves constrained optimization subject to a fixed position along the reaction coordinate. A number of schemes for doing this have been proposed, and these

---

6. *SPARTAN* allows animation along normal coordinates.

are collectively termed **Intrinsic Reaction Coordinate** methods.[7] Note that none of these schemes are unique; while the transition state is a well defined point of the overall potential energy surface, there are an infinite number of pathways linking it to reactant and product molecules.

A word of encouragement: "incorrect" transition states located by calculation, that is, not linking the expected reactant to the expected product, may indicate new chemistry. Don't discard them so quickly!

3.6 How similar are transition state geometries obtained from different levels of calculation?

The complete lack of experimental structural information precludes any direct assessment of the ability of calculations to properly describe the geometries of transition states. For *ab initio* models, we can look for convergence of geometrical parameters as a function of the level of calculation, i.e., treatment of electron correlation and basis set, and to compare the results from any given method with those of the apparent "limit". Unfortunately, we do not have a similar tool in dealing with semi-empirical or even density functional models. Changes in parameters in the former and changes in the form of the functionals in the latter do not tend toward obvious limits. (Improvements in basis set for a given functional in the case of density functional methods should converge to a limit.) It is not obvious from first principles how to choose "better" parameters or "better" functionals at least in a systematic manner! All we can do in these cases is to compare results with those from high-level *ab initio* models.

Key geometrical parameters for transition states for a number of simple organic reactions calculated using AM1, HF/3-21G[(*)], HF/6-31G* and (where available) MP2/6-31G* levels are provided in **Table 3-3**. It is immediately apparent that these transition state geometries vary much more widely as a function of level of calculation than do equilibrium geometries. Bond distance changes of 0.1 Å are common even among the three *ab initio* methods, and even larger variations are noted for comparisons involving AM1. (Variations in bond lengths among the various theoretical models for corresponding equilibrium species are seldom greater than 0.02-0.03Å.) Still, all models yield qualitatively similar results insofar as overall structure.

The quantitative results here provide some rationale for the suggestion made earlier (**Section 3.3**), that it is generally of benefit to precede transition state optimization at *ab initio* levels by optimization using semi-empirical models. The data also suggest the utility of using low-level (Hartree-Fock) models to furnish initial transition state geometries for higher-level (Hartree-Fock and correlated) models.

A word of warning: semi-empirical methods sometimes yield transition states which are completely unrealistic. Be certain to carefully examine the results of such studies for obvious problems.

---

7. See for example: C. Gonzalez and H.B. Schlegel, J. Phys. Chem, **90**, 2154 (1989). *SPARTAN* allows construction of intrinsic reaction coordinates by way of user imposed constraints.

Table 3-3: Key Geometrical Parameters for Transition States for Simple Organic Reactions

transition state for	geometrical parameter	AM1	HF/3-21G(*)	HF/6-31G*	MP2/6-31G*
rearrangement of methylisocyanide to acetonitrile	$r(C_1C_2)$	1.700	1.871	1.741	1.752
	$r(C_1N)$	1.803	1.986	1.896	1.855
	$r(C_2N)$	1.226	1.187	1.174	1.205

pyrolysis of ethyl formate	$r(C_1O_1)$	1.295	1.275	1.248	1.279
	$r(C_1O_2)$	1.284	1.252	1.234	1.266
	$r(C_2O_2)$	1.762	1.966	2.096	1.979
	$r(C_2C_3)$	1.407	1.402	1.396	1.396
	$r(C_3H)$	1.444	1.403	1.312	1.337
	$r(O_1H)$	1.181	1.238	1.327	1.288

Cope rearrangement of 1,5-hexadiene	$r(C_1C_2) =$ $r(C_5C_6) =$ $r(C_2C_3) =$ $r(C_4C_5)$	1.427	1.389	1.390	—
	$r(C_1C_6) =$ $r(C_3C_4)$	1.646	2.021	2.047	—

Claisen rearrangement of allyl, vinyl ether	$r(C_1C_2)$	1.429	1.388	1.389	—
	$r(C_1O)$	1.580	1.877	1.918	—
	$r(C_2C_3)$	1.400	1.382	1.376	—
	$r(C_3C_4)$	1.845	2.139	2.266	—
	$r(C_4C_5)$	1.407	1.374	1.374	—
	$r(C_5O)$	1.323	1.290	1.262	—

Table 3-3: Key Geometrical Parameters for Transition States for Simple Organic Reactions (continued)

transition state for	geometrical parameter	AM1	HF/ 3-21G(*)	HF/ 6-31G*	MP2/ 6-31G*
Diels-Alder cycloaddition of cyclopentadiene and acrylonitrile	$r(C_1C_2)$	1.420	1.388	1.395	—
	$r(C_1C_5)$	1.521	1.522	1.510	—
	$r(C_1C_7)$	2.026	2.131	2.092	—
	$r(C_2C_3)$	1.410	1.400	1.392	—
	$r(C_3C_4)$	1.411	1.380	1.384	—
	$r(C_4C_5)$	1.514	1.513	1.501	—
	$r(C_4C_6)$	2.214	2.289	2.315	—
	$r(C_6C_7)$	1.399	1.379	1.391	—
ene reaction (1-pentene)	$r(C_1C_2)$	1.410	1.402	1.400	—
	$r(C_2C_3)$	1.385	1.374	1.377	—
	$r(C_3C_4)$	2.205	2.110	2.120	—
	$r(C_4C_5)$	1.399	1.397	1.398	—
	$r(C_1H)$	1.330	1.350	1.363	—
	$r(C_5H)$	1.438	1.447	1.444	—
pyrolysis of oxacyclohexenone	$r(C_1C_2)$	1.711	1.884	1.739	—
	$r(C_1O_1)$	1.250	1.226	1.218	—
	$r(C_1O_2)$	1.228	1.199	1.195	—
	$r(C_2C_3)$	1.411	1.403	1.425	—
	$r(C_3C_4)$	1.401	1.386	1.384	—
	$r(C_4C_5)$	1.372	1.369	1.371	—
	$r(C_5O_1)$	2.246	2.124	2.263	—
pyrolysis of cyclopentenesulfone	$r(C_1C_2)$ = $r(C_3C_4)$	1.390	1.390	1.392	—
	$r(C_1S)$ = $r(C_4S)$	2.220	2.331	2.328	—
	$r(C_2C_3)$	1.402	1.385	1.385	—
	$r(SO)$	1.428	1.428	1.426	—

Table 3-3: Key Geometrical Parameters for Transition States for Simple Organic Reactions (continued)

transition state for	geometrical parameter	AM1	HF/ 3-21G[(*)]	HF/ 6-31G*	MP2/ 6-31G*
addition of singlet difluorocarbene and ethylene	$r(C_1C_2)$	1.703	1.735	1.748	1.897
	$r(C_1C_3)$	2.321	2.159	2.195	2.514
	$r(C_2C_3)$	1.383	1.386	1.371	1.376
	$r(C_1F)$	1.329	1.356	1.321	1.341
cycloaddition of formonitrile oxide and acetylene	$r(C_1C_2)$	1.229	1.213	1.214	1.243
	$r(C_1O)$	2.313	2.131	2.213	2.205
	$r(C_2C_3)$	1.946	2.269	2.147	2.077
	$r(C_3N)$	1.254	1.162	1.174	1.239
	$r(NO)$	1.195	1.308	1.222	1.222
addition of difluoroborane and ethylene	$r(C_1C_2)$	1.406	1.406	1.393	1.395
	$r(C_2B)$	1.730	1.740	1.759	1.766
	$r(BF)$	1.330	1.385	1.360	1.380
	$r(C_1H)$	1.707	1.693	1.661	1.645
	$r(BH)$	1.278	1.278	1.275	1.269
1,5 hydrogen migration in 1,3-pentadiene	$r(C_1C_2) = r(C_4C_5)$	1.408	1.405	1.406	—
	$r(C_2C_3) = r(C_3C_4)$	1.392	1.386	1.387	—
	$r(C_1H) = r(C_5H)$	1.416	1.448	1.443	—

Table 3-3: Key Geometrical Parameters for Transition States for Simple Organic Reactions (continued)

transition state for	geometrical parameter	AM1	HF/ 3-21G$^{(*)}$	HF/ 6-31G*	MP2/ 6-31G*
1,7 hydrogen migration in 1,3,5-heptatriene	$r(C_1C_2) =$ $r(C_6C_7)$	1.403	1.397	1.399	—
	$r(C_2C_3) =$ $r(C_5C_6)$	1.385	1.383	1.387	—
	$r(C_3C_4) =$ $r(C_4C_5)$	1.390	1.392	1.396	—
	$r(C_1H) =$ $r(C_7H)$	1.366	1.376	1.383	—

3.7 How similar are transition state geometries for functionally-related reactions?

The fact that closely related molecules usually exhibit structural similarities has long been recognized by chemists and is, of course, the reason behind the remarkable success of empirical ("molecular mechanics") schemes to accurately account for molecular equilibrium geometry. The extent to which transition states for functionally related reactions are also structurally similar is not really known, and cannot be known at least in any detail from experiment. Some degree of similarity is to be expected (after all, transition states are molecules), although perhaps not to the extent as exhibited by equilibrium species (the bonding in transition states is presumed to be weaker than the bonding in stable molecules and, because of this, structural variations should be greater). Calculations provide the only opportunity to clarify the issue.

Aside from the obvious pedagodical reason for wishing to understand in detail systematics in transition-state geometries, there is a very practical motive for our interest. Were transition states for closely related reactions to show a high degree of structural similarity, and were we able to anticipate changes in transition state geometries with subtle changes in the nature of the reaction, i.e., remote substitution or changes in regio- and/or stereochemistry, then we would be able to accurately guess transition state geometries in advance of actually doing any optimization. This is of course, what we are now able to do for equilibrium structures, and is the primary reason why optimization of equilibrium geometry is both highly efficient and routine.

Key geometrical features of transition states for a few sets of closely related reactions are shown in **Figure 3-1**. Results from AM1 semi-empirical and both 3-21G$^{(*)}$ and 6-31G* *ab initio* calculations have been examined. Other semi-empirical and *ab initio* models, as well as density functional and correlated models, would be expected to yield qualitatively similar results.

The first comparison, pyrolysis of ethyl formate vs. pyrolysis of cyclohexylformate, shows considerable variation in transition state geometries for all three levels of calculation. It is interesting to note that the differences are not readily interpretable in terms of usual notions of "lateness" of transition states. While the position of the migrating hydrogen in the two transition states suggests that reaction of ethyl formate has proceeded further, the opposite conclusion follows from examination of the CO single bond which is breaking. All these levels of calculation show similar differences between the two transition states, an observation which we should be able to put to practical use.

Relatively little variation is seen in the transition state geometries for singlet dichlorocarbene addition to ethylene and to cyclohexene, for all three sets of calculations. As before, the different calculations closely parallel each other with regard to changes in transition state geometries.

Perhaps the most interesting (and potentially most important) case is exemplified by Diels-Alder cycloaddition reactions involving cyclopentadiene and methylcyclopentadiene. These reflect both subtle changes in substitution and even more subtle changes in stereochemistry of reaction. All three transition states considered are nearly identical at each level of calculation. (As in the other reactions, AM1, 3-21G$^{(*)}$ and 6-31G* transition state geometries do

Figure 3-1: AM1, 3-21G⁽*⁾ and 6-31G* Transition States for Related Reactions

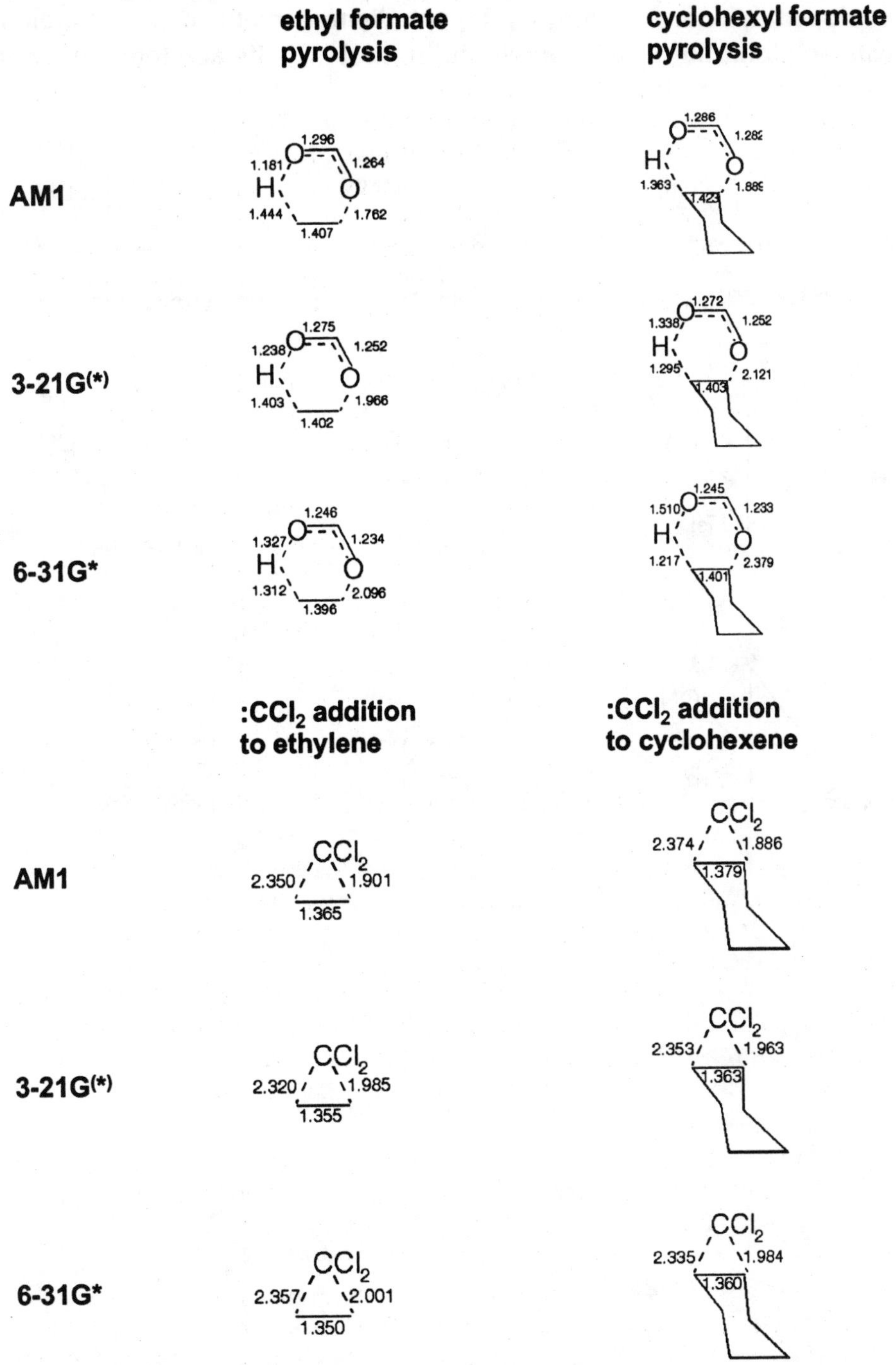

Diels-Alder cycloadditions.

| cyclopentadiene with acrylonitrile | methylcyclopentadiene with acrylonitrile (*exo*) | methylcyclopentadiene with acrylonitrile (*endo*) |

AM1

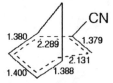
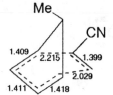
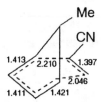

3-21G(*)

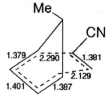
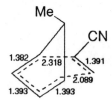
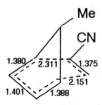

6-31G*

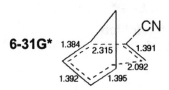
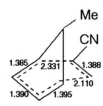

differ significantly from each other.) Even the transition state corresponding to the relatively crowded *syn* cycloaddition of methylcyclopentadiene with acrylonitrile differs from the others only slightly.

While we have not presented sufficient examples to allow meaningful generalizations to be made, these results support the conclusion that that treatment of model systems in advance of real systems should lead to some reduction in overall computational effort. Evidence for this has already been presented in **Section 3.3**. As we earlier stressed, the lesson is to make use of model systems wherever possible.

3.8 Is it always necessary to utilize "exact" transition state geometries in determining activation energies, or will geometries obtained from lower-level calculations suffice?

This is a similar question to that already posed regarding the use of approximate equilibrium geometries for thermochemical comparisons (see **Section 2-9**). As is the previous case, it is an issue of balancing the possible magnitude of errors introduced as a result of using approximate geometries vs. the potentially enormous savings in computer time realized by employing low-level models to establish structure, in particular the structure of the transition state. One might anticipate that the chance of success here is somewhat less than that in dealing with equilibrium (thermodynamic) comparisons. Afterall, semi-empirical models, as well as low-level *ab initio* and (local) density functional models are known to have some problems in accounting for transition-state geometries in all cases. It is, however, even more valuable than the corresponding situation for equilibrium properties due to the greater difficulty of obtaining transition states.

The data in **Tables 3-4** to **3-16**, illustrate for a small but diverse series of organic reactions the magnitudes of the errors in activation energy introduced because of the use of approximate geometries. For each reaction, activation energies have been calculated using Hartree-Fock models with the $3\text{-}21G^{(*)}$, $6\text{-}31G^*$ and $6\text{-}311\text{+}G(2d,p)$ basis sets, density functional models with the same basis sets and three different functionals (SVWN, BLYP and B3LYP) and MP2 models again with the same three basis sets. Reactant and transition state geometries have been obtained at four different levels: semi-empirical AM1, Hartree-Fock $3\text{-}21G^{(*)}$ and $6\text{-}31G^*$ and (where practical) correlated MP2/6-$31G^*$ models.

More than the usual number of computational models are examined here. In particular, the $6\text{-}311\text{+}G(2d,p)$ basis set is included, not because it is practical, but rather because it closely approaches a limiting representation. The BLYP density functional model has been examined as an alternative to the SVWN and B3LYP methods dealt with throughout this book. Experience suggests that it should be able to account for known dificiencies of local density functional (SVWN) models, yet it does not require calculation of the Hartree-Fock exchange as does the B3LYP functional. The absence of direct experimental data with which to compare makes selection of appropriate theoretical model difficult, and we want to be assured that any conclusions regarding choice of geometry extend to a variety of different methods.

Table 3-4: Effect of Choice of Geometry on Activation Energy for Rearrangement of Methylisocyanide to Acetonitrile

level of calculation	geometry of reactant/transition state			
	AM1	HF/3-21G	HF/6-31G*	MP2/6-31G*
HF/3-21G	64	58	—	—
6-31G*	48	48	46	—
6-311+G(2d,p)	47	45	44	—
SVWN/3-21G	53	51	—	—
6-31G*	42	44	40	41
6-311+G(2d,p)	41	43	39	40
BLYP/3-21G	51	46	—	—
6-31G*	43	39	38	39
6-311+G(2d,p)	40	38	37	38
B3LYP/3-21G	55	49	—	—
6-31G*	42	42	40	41
6-311+G(2d,p)	42	41	39	40
MP2/3-21G	57	51	—	—
6-31G*	43	44	42	43
6-311+G(2d,p)	43	43	41	42

Table 3-5: Effect of Choice of Geometry on Activation Energy for Pyrolysis of Ethyl Formate

level of calculation	geometry of reactant/transition state			
	AM1	HF/3-21G	HF/6-31G*	MP2/6-31G*
HF/3-21G	63	62	—	—
6-31G*	75	71	70	—
6-311+G(2d,p)	72	67	66	—
SVWN/3-21G	40	38	—	—
6-31G*	49	46	47	46
6-311+G(2d,p)	45	42	43	42
BLYP/3-21G	43	40	—	—
6-31G*	53	47	46	47
6-311+G(2d,p)	49	44	42	43
B3LYP/3-21G	49	46	—	—
6-31G*	58	53	53	53
6-311+G(2d,p)	54	50	49	49
MP2/3-21G	57	55	—	—
6-31G*	64	60	61	60
6-311+G(2d,p)	58	55	56	54

Table 3-6: Effect of Choice of Geometry on Activation Energy for Cope Rearrangement of 1,5 Hexadiene

level of calculation	geometry of reactant/transition state		
	AM1	HF/3-21G	HF/6-31G*
HF/3-21G	65	45	—
6-31G*	71	56	56
6-311+G(2d,p)	73	57	57
SVWN/3-21G	19	17	—
6-31G*	23	23	24
6-311+G(2d,p)	25	23	24
BLYP/3-21G	35	25	—
6-31G*	39	30	30
6-311+G(2d,p)	41	30	30
B3LYP/3-21G	39	28	—
6-31G*	43	34	34
6-311+G(2d,p)	45	35	35
MP2/3-21G	38	28	—
6-31G*	34	31	31

Table 3-7: Effect of Choice of Geometry on Activation Energy for Claisen Rearrangement of Allyl, Vinyl Ether

level of calculation	geometry of reactant/transition state		
	AM1	HF/3-21G	HF/6-31G*
HF/3-21G	52	41	—
6-31G*	60	47	48
6-311+G(2d,p)	61	48	48
SVWN/3-21G	17	13	—
6-31G*	22	19	22
6-311+G(2d,p)	23	19	22
BLYP/3-21G	29	18	—
6-31G*	34	23	22
6-311+G(2d,p)	35	23	22
B3LYP/3-21G	31	22	—
6-31G*	37	27	28
6-311+G(2d,p)	39	28	28
MP2/3-21G	32	21	—
6-31G*	31	23	25

Table 3-8: Effect of Choice of Geometry on Activation Energy for Diels Alder Cycloaddition of Cyclopentadiene and Ethylene

level of calculation	geometry of reactant/transition state		
	AM1	HF/3-21G	HF/6-31G*
HF/3-21G	29	30	—
6-31G*	41	40	40
6-311+G(2d,p)	45	44	44
SVWN/3-21G	−14	−11	—
6-31G*	−5	−4	−4
6-311+G(2d,p)	−2	−1	−1
BLYP/3-21G	12	12	—
6-31G*	20	19	18
6-311+G(2d,p)	25	23	23
B3LYP/3-21G	12	12	—
6-31G*	21	20	19
6-311+G(2d,p)	25	23	23
MP2/3-21G	11	11	—
6-31G*	12	11	11

Table 3-9: Effect of Choice of Geometry on Activation Energy for Formonitrile Oxide to Acetylene

level of calculation	geometry of reactant/transition state			
	AM1	HF/3-21G	HF/6-31G*	MP2/6-31G*
HF/3-21G	31	25	—	—
6-31G*	37	35	35	—
6-311+G(2d,p)	40	37	38	—
SVWN/3-21G	–7	–6	—	—
6-31G*	–7	–2	–6	–8
6-311+G(2d,p)	–2	1	–2	–5
BLYP/3-21G	7	8	—	—
6-31G*	7	12	8	6
6-311+G(2d,p)	12	16	13	11
B3LYP/3-21G	10	10	–	—
6-31G*	11	15	12	10
6-311+G(2d,p)	16	18	16	14
MP2/3-21G	20	12		—
6-31G*	17	15	11	8
6-311+G(2d,p)	17	14	11	8

Table 3-10: Effect of Choice of Geometry on Activation Energy for 1,5-Hydrogen Shift in 1-Pentene

level of calculation	geometry of reactant/transition state			
	AM1	HF/3-21G	HF/6-31G*	MP2/6-31G*
HF/3-21G	74	75	—	—
6-31G*	84	84	84	—
6-311+G(2d,p)	83	83	83	—
SVWN/3-21G	43	44	—	—
6-31G*	47	47	48	48
6-311+G(2d,p)	45	45	46	46
BLYP/3-21G	47	48	—	—
6-31G*	51	51	51	51
6-311+G(2d,p)	49	50	50	50
B3LYP/3-21G	52	53	—	—
6-31G*	57	58	58	58
6-311+G(2d,p)	56	56	56	56
MP2/3-21G	56	57	—	—
6-31G*	60	61	61	60

Table 3-11: Effect of Choice of Geometry on Activation Energy for Addition of Singlet Difluorocarbene to Ethylene

level of calculation	geometry of reactant/transition state			
	AM1	HF/3-21G	HF/6-31G*	MP2/6-31G*
HF/3-21G	30	27	—	—
6-31G*	33	31	31	—
6-311+G(2d,p)	34	31	32	—
SVWN/3-21G	−20	−19	—	—
6-31G*	−15	−15	−14	−10
6-311+G(2d,p)	−13	−13	−12	−8
BLYP/3-21G	1	1	—	—
6-31G*	5	5	5	5
6-311+G(2d,p)	8	9	9	8
B3LYP/3-21G	4	4	—	—
6-31G*	7	8	8	8
6-311+G(2d,p)	10	10	11	10
MP2/3-21G	14	14	—	—
6-31G*	9	10	10	12
6-311+G(2d,p)	8	8	9	11

Table 3-12: Effect of Choice of Geometry on Activation Energy for Addition of Difluoroborane to Ethylene

level of calculation	geometry of reactant/transition state			
	AM1	HF/3-21G	HF/6-31G*	MP2/6-31G*
HF/3-21G	39	35	—	—
6-31G*	42	39	39	—
6-311+G(2d,p)	43	40	40	—
SVWN/3-21G	6	1	—	—
6-31G*	7	3	2	2
6-311+G(2d,p)	9	6	4	3
BLYP/3-21G	29	24	—	—
6-31G*	31	27	26	27
6-311+G(2d,p)	31	29	28	29
B3LYP/3-21G	27	23	—	—
6-31G*	30	26	25	26
6-311+G(2d,p)	32	28	28	28
MP2/3-21G	39	33	—	—
6-31G*	33	28	27	27
6-311+G(2d,p)	32	28	27	27

Table 3-13: Effect of Choice of Geometry on Activation Energy for Extrusion of Carbon Dioxide from Oxacyclohexenone

	geometry of reactant/transition state		
level of calculation	AM1	HF/3-21G	HF/6-31G*
HF/3-21G	56	59	—
6-31G*	55	61	60
6-311+G(2d,p)	53	60	58
SVWN/3-21G	38	39	—
6-31G*	39	42	42
6-311+G(2d,p)	37	40	40
BLYP/3-21G	28	29	—
6-31G*	29	31	31
6-311+G(2d,p)	26	29	28
B3LYP/3-21G	37	38	—
6-31G*	37	40	40
6-311+G(2d,p)	35	38	38
MP2/3-21G	41	39	—
6-31G*	43	43	45

Table 3-14: Effect of Choice of Geometry on Activation Energy for Extrusion of Sulfur Dioxide from Cyclopentensulfone

	geometry of reactant/transition state		
level of calculation	AM1	HF/3-21G	HF/6-31G*
HF/3-21G	43	49	—
6-31G*	41	49	49
6-311+G(2d,p)	42	48	48
SVWN/3-21G	16	27	—
6-31G*	14	26	26
6-311+G(2d,p)	17	26	27
BLYP/3-21G	0	13	—
6-31G*	–2	11	12
6-311+G(2d,p)	0	11	12
B3LYP/3-21G	12	23	—
6-31G*	10	22	22
6-311+G(2d,p)	12	21	22
MP2/3-21G	15	25	—
6-31G*	16	26	27

Table 3-15: Effect of Choice of Geometry on Activation Energy for Pyrolysis of Dimethyl, ethylamine oxide

level of calculation	geometry of reactant/transition state		
	AM1	HF/3-21G	HF/6-31G*
HF/3-21G	22	36	—
6-31G*	41	43	45
6-311+G(2d,p)	40	41	44
SVWN/3-21G	5	7	17
6-31G*	18	13	17
6-311+G(2d,p)	18	13	
			—
BLYP/3-21G	11	12	21
6-31G*	24	18	21
6-311+G(2d,p)	23	18	
			—
B3LYP/3-21G	12	16	26
6-31G*	27	22	26
6-311+G(2d,p)	26	22	
			—
MP2/3-21G	14	20	—
6-31G*	29	26	30

Table 3-16: Effect of Choice of Geometry on Activation Energy for [2,3] Sigmatropic Rearrangement of Allylsulfoxide

level of calculation	geometry of reactant/transition state			
	AM1	HF/3-21G	HF/6-31G*	MP2/6-31G*
HF/3-21G	27	24	—	—
6-31G*	39	31	33	—
6-311+G(2d,p)	43	34	36	—
SVWN/3-21G	1	3	—	—
6-31G*	9	7	8	10
6-311+G(2d,p)	14	10	12	13
BLYP/3-21G	5	3	—	—
6-31G*	14	7	8	10
6-311+G(2d,p)	19	10	12	13
B3LYP/3-21G	9	8	—	—
6-31G*	19	12	13	14
6-311+G(2d,p)	23	15	17	18
MP2/3-21G	12	10	—	—
6-31G*	19	15	16	17

The most obvious conclusion from the data is that both Hartree-Fock geometries and the MP2 geometry lead to very similar activation energies for all levels of calculation considered. Errors are typically in the range of 1-2 kcal/mol and seldom exceed 4 kcal/mol. The only serious exception occurs for 1,3-dipolar cycloaddition of formonitrile oxide with acetylene. Subject to recognition that the reactions presented here certainly do not adequately span the full range of possible processes, it is clear that even low-level Hartree-Fock models provide a credible account of the geometries both of reactants and transition states, and that the errors resulting from their use are consistently small. They should be used for this purpose wherever possible.

On the other hand, activation energies calculated assuming AM1 reactant and transition-state geometries sometimes differ significantly from those obtained from HF/3-21G$^{(*)}$, HF/6-31G* and MP2/6-31G* structures. The largest deviations are on the order of 10 kcal/mol, clearly an unacceptable error, although in about half the reactions considered the deviations are only on the order of 2-3 kcal/mol. Use of semi-empirical structures for the purpose of calculating absolute activation energies must, therefore, proceed only with some caution; only after acceptable results are achieved with model systems should they be trusted for related reactions.

In **Section 5.1**, we comment more on the differences between activation energies obtained using different theoretical models, and of the relationship between calculated and experimental activation energies. It is clear from examination of the present data, however, that absolute activation energies are very sensitive to the choice of method, including choice of basis set. Note in particular, that Hartree-Fock models generally yield activation energies which are larger than those from (non-local) density functional and MP2 models. Note also that local density functional (SVWN) models yield very low (and sometimes negative!) activation energies. Finally, note that activation energies obtained from 3-21G$^{(*)}$ basis set calculations for all levels of theory are generally different (lower) than those obtained using the 6-31G* and 6-311+G(2d,p) basis sets. The point we want to make is that differences due to the use of different theoretical models are generally much larger than any changes resulting from the use of "approximate", i.e., from lower-level models, geometries. We urge the use of low-level geometries wherever possible in studies of activation energies, subject only to careful examination of model systems.

3.9 Is it always necessary to utilize "exact" transition state geometries in determining relative activation energies needed to evaluate substituent effects on reaction rates or regio- and stereochemical product distributions, or will geometries from lower level calculations suffice?

We have seen in the previous section that approximate geometries obtained from low-level *ab initio* methods are generally suitable for use in calculating absolute activation energies for a variety of different chemical reactions. On the other hand, semi-empirical AM1 geometries do not provide an entirely reliable account. The question posed here is slightly different and probably much more important: are approximate geometries suitable for use in calculating relative activation energies among closely related processes? The question is different because the small errors introduced by use of approximate geometries (typically in the range of 1-3 kcal/mol) may now be of the same order of magnitude as the energy differences under investigation, although one might hope for cancellation of errors. The question is important, because very frequently relative activation energies are the quantities of interest. The most conspicuous cases occur in dealing with remote substitution effects and with the distribution of regio-and stereochemical products of chemical reactions.

Table 3-17 considers the effect of geometry on the calculated activation energies for Diels-Alder cycloadditions of cyclopentadiene (acting as a diene) with a variety of cyano-substituted olefins (acting as dienophiles), relative to the *endo* addition with acrylonitrile as a standard. Energies have been evaluated at the HF/6-31G* level, with reactant and product geometries obtained from semi-empirical AM1 and Hartree-Fock STO-3G and 3-21G calculations, as well as from HF/6-31G* calculations ("exact" geometries). (Discussion of the performance of the various models with regard to calculation of relative activation energies is provided in **Section 5.2**.) We examine the performance of semi-empirical calculations to furnish structure (even though they proved unreliable for use in calculating absolute activation energies), in the hope that the subtle differences here will lead in large part to cancellation of errors.

The data clearly suggest that all models, including the AM1 model, provide suitable geometries for the calculation of relative activation energies in these systems. The largest error introduced is only 1 kcal/mol. The implication is that proper description of the relative activation energetics of reactions which differ from each other only in details of substitution can be obtained using approximate geometries. Unfortunately, the experimental data in this case do not distinguish between *endo* and *exo* pathways, so it is not possible to say whether the use of approximate geometries is adequate for the assignment of stereochemistry in these reactions.

The effect of choice of geometry on regio- and stereochemical preferences in Diels-Alder reactions is examined in **Tables 3-18** and **3-19**, respectively. Again, energies have been evaluated at the HF/6-31G* level and three sets of approximate geometries (AM1, HF/STO-3G and HF/3-21G) have been examined, in addition to "exact" geometries. (The performance of various theoretical models in describing regio- and stereochemical preferences is discussed in **Section 5.2**.) Again, calculations based on semi-empirical structures have been included with the hope of error cancellation.

The results here again suggest that use of approximate geometries does not significantly alter the results of "full calculations". In the case of regiochemical comparisons (**Table 3-18**), use of even AM1 geometries introduces errors of only a few tenths of a kcal/mol, and errors incurred as a result of use of HF/STO-3G and HF/3-21G structures are even smaller. The errors in the case of stereochemical comparisons (**Table 3-19**) are somewhat larger, but in the view of this author, are still within acceptable limits. Here, the low-level *ab initio* geometries appear to provide a somewhat better account than the semi-empirical structures, although the differences are not really large.

The overall recommendation following from these types of comparisons is very clear: use approximate geometries for calculations of relative activation energies among closely related systems. While other examples need to be provided in order to fully generalize such a recommendation (there will no

Table 3-17: Effect of Choice of Geometry on Relative Activation Energies of Diels-Alder Cycloadditions of Cyclopentadiene with Electron-Deficient Dienophiles. 6-31G* Calculations.

dienophile	stereochemistry of adduct	geometry of reactant/transition state				expt.
		AM1	STO-3G	3-21G	6-31G*	
ethylene		4	4	4	4	8.5
cyanoethylene	endo	0	0	0	0	0
	exo	0	0	0	0	0
trans-1,2-dicyanoethylene		-4	-3	-3	-3	-2.6
cis-1,2-dicyanoethylene	endo	-4	-3	-3	-3	-3.8
	exo	-3	-3	-3	-3	-3.8
1,1-dicyanoethylene		-7	-7	-7	-8	-7.2
tricyanoethylene	endo	-9	-9	-9	-9	-9.2
	exo	-9	-9	-8	-9	-9.2
tetracyanoethylene		-12	-11	-11	-11	-11.2

Table 3-18: Effect of Choice of Geometry on Regioselectivity in Additions of Substituted Cyclopentadienes with Acrylonitrile[a]. 6-31G* Calculations.

diene substituent		geometry of transition state			
	AM1	STO-3G	3-21G	6-31G*	expt.
1-methyl	1.1 (o)	1.2 (o)	1.2 (o)	1.3 (o)	o
1-methoxy	3.4 (o)	3.7 (o)	3.8 (o)	4.2 (o)	o
2-methyl	0.7 (p)	0.6 (p)	0.6 (p)	0.6 (p)	p
2-methoxy	3.6(p)	3.9 (p)	3.8 (p)	4.0 (p)	p

a) o = *ortho* product; p = *para* product.

Table 3-19: Effect of Choice of Geometry on *Syn-Anti* Selectivity in Additions of 5-Substituted Cyclopentadienes with Electron-Deficient Dienophiles.[a] 6-31G* Calculations.

diene substituent	dienophile	geometry at transition state			
		AM1	STO-3G	3-21G$^{(*)}$	6-31G*
CH_3	ethylene	1.2 (a)	1.2 (a)	0.7 (a)	0.8 (a)
	acrylonitrile	1.8 (a)	1.4 (a)	0.9 (a)	1.1 (a)
	cis-1,2-dicyanoethylene	2.0 (a)	1.5 (a)	1.1 (a)	1.2 (a)
	tetracyanoethylene	7.3 (a)	6.0 (a)	5.4 (a)	5.6 (a)
Cl	ethylene	0	0.1 (a)	0.6 (a)	0.5 (s)
	acrylonitrile	0.8 (s)	1.2 (s)	1.5 (s)	1.5 (s)
	cis-1,2-dicyanoethylene	1.6 (s)	2.2 (s)	2.4 (s)	2.4 (s)
	tetracyanoethylene	7.9 (a)	5.8 (a)	5.0 (a)	5.0 (a)

a) s ≡ *syn* addition; a ≡ *anti* addition.

doubt be exceptions), and while calibration studies should be completed before widespread applications, the savings which might be achieved by such a strategy are considerable.

3.10 Are there chemical reactions for which transition states do not exist?

Surprisingly enough, the answer to this question is yes. In fact, reactions without barriers and discernible transition states are quite common. Two radicals will typically combine without activation, for example, two methyl radicals to form ethane.

$$H_3C\cdot + \cdot CH_3 \rightarrow H_3C - CH_3$$

Radicals will often add to paired-electron species with no (or very small) activation, for example, methyl radical and ethylene to yield 1-propyl radical.

$$H_3C\cdot + H_2C=CH_2 \ H_3C\text{-}CH_2\text{-}CH_2\cdot$$

In the gas phase, addition of ions to neutral molecules will almost always occur without activation energy, for example, addition of *tert* butyl cation to benzene to yield a stable "benzenium" ion.

A more familiar example is S_N2 addition of an anionic nucleophile to an aklyl halide. In the gas phase, this occurs without activation, and the known barrier for the process in solution is a solvent effect (see **Section 5.3**).

Finally, reactions of highly electron-deficient species, including reactions of transition metal complexes, often occur with little if any activation energy required. Such well known processes as hydroboration and β-hydride elimination are likely candidates under the right circumstances.

Failure to find a transition state, but instead location of what appears to be a stable intermediate or even the final product, does not necessarily mean failure of the computational model (nor does it rule this out). It may simply mean that there is no transition state! Unfortunately it is very difficult to tell which is the true situation.

An interesting question is why reactions without activation barriers actually occur at different overall rates. The reason has to do with the pre-exponential term in the rate expression, which tells us something both about the frequency of collisions and their overall effectiveness. These factors depend on molecular geometry and accessibility of reagents.

3.11 To what extent does solvent affect transition state structure?

There is not yet sufficient experience to provide a general answer to this question. Remarks made earlier (**Section 2.13**) about the influence of solvent on equilibrium structure would likely also apply here, and suggest that solvent will have little effect on the geometries of neutral transition states and perhaps play a somewhat larger role on the structures of charged transition states. Solvent is also likely to affect transition state tautomer selection, and in particular is likely to favor charge-separated tautomers over "neutral" tautomers.

Solvent would be expected to exert a considerable effect over reaction energetics, and favor species in which charge is localized rather than delocalized. We discuss this later in **Section 5.3**. Solvent might also effect changes in preferred conformation both of reagents and transition state. This is addressed in **Section 6.7**.

4

Making Use of Energy Data for Thermochemical Comparisons

Aside from geometry, energy is the most common quantity demanded from calculations. Unlike geometry, which is generally well described even by semi-empirical methods and low-level *ab initio* schemes as well as higher-level models, experience suggests that energy comparisons are much more subject to large uncertainties, and that for some types of comparisons very high levels of calculation, making use of large basis sets and taking account for electron correlation, may be required. In this chapter, we describe and briefly illustrate the performance of various levels of calculation for different classes of energy comparisons. Our objective is to sort out those types of reactions which will likely be difficult to describe from types of processes which will be well accounted for using simple theoretical models applicable to investigations involving large molecules. Our discussion is brief and very limited in scope. Further remarks appear in **Appendix A**, and thorough coverage has been provided elsewhere.[1]

We start out (**Section 4.1**) with a breakdown of chemical reactions into four categories depending on the extent to which electron pairs and electron-pair bonds are conserved, and very briefly comment on the performance of the various levels of calculation with respect to each of these classes of reactions. The use of *isodesmic* reactions, processes in which the number of each kind of formal bond is conserved, to obtain heats of formation is explored in **Section 4.2**. A critique of the use of correlated models, including density functional

---

1. (a) W.J. Hehre, L. Radom, P.v.R. Schleyer and J.A. Pople, **Ab Initio Molecular Orbital Theory,** Chapter 6, Wiley, New York, 1986; (b) W.J. Hehre, **Critical Assessment of Modern Electronic Structure Methods,** Wavefunction, Irvine, California, 1995.

models, to describe the energetics of reactions in which the total number of bonds is conserved is provided in **Section 4.3**. A surprising conclusion is that correlated models may actually not be as satisfactory as Hartree-Fock schemes, unless very large basis sets are employed.

We defer the issue of solvent effects on the energetics of gas-phase processes to **Section 5.3**, where we combine it with a brief discussion of the role of solvent in altering activation barriers and reaction profiles in general.

4.1 What levels of calculation are required for accurate descriptions of reaction thermochemistry?

Thermochemical comparisons may conveniently be placed into one of several categories depending on the extent to which bonds and non-bonded lone pairs are conserved (**Table 4-1**). This distinction is important as the theoretical models which we have been discussing differ most in the way that they treat electron correlation, i.e., the coupling of motions of electrons. (Correlation effects would be expected to be most important for electrons which are paired.) Hartree-Fock models completely ignore correlation, while density functional and MP2 models take partial explicit account of electron correlation. Semi-empirical methods have, of course, been parameterized to reproduce ex-perimental data, and so may be thought of as methods in which electron correlation is taken into account implicitly.

At one extreme are processes in which not even the total number of electron pairs (bonds and non-bonded lone pairs) is conserved. Homolytic bond dissociation processes, e.g.,

$$H\!-\!F \rightarrow H\!\cdot + F\!\cdot \qquad\qquad \text{homolytic bond dissociation}$$

are an obvious example. Comparisons of transition states and reactants (as required for the calculation of absolute activation energies) are also likely candidates for processes in which the total number of electron pairs is not conserved. Discussion is provided in **Section 5.1**. Less drastic are reactions in which the total number of electron pairs is maintained, but chemical bonds are converted to non-bonded lone pairs or vice versa. Heterolytic bond dissocia-tion reactions, e.g.,

$$Na\!-\!F \rightarrow Na^+ + \ddot{F} \qquad\qquad \text{heterolytic bond dissociation}$$

and some kinds of structural isomerizations, e.g.,

$$H_2C\ddot{n}\,O \rightarrow HC\ddot{O}H \qquad\qquad \text{structural isomerism}$$

are good examples. Even more "gentle" are reactions in which both the number of bonds and the number of non-bonded lone pairs are conserved. This type of reaction is very commonly encountered. Several examples are given below.

$$H_2C\ddot{n}\,CH_2 + 2H_2 \rightarrow 2CH_4 \qquad\qquad \text{hydrogenation}$$

$$CH_2CH_2CH_2 \rightarrow CH_3CH\,\ddot{n}\,CH_2 \qquad\qquad \text{structural isomerism}$$

Table 4-1: Performance of Theoretical Models for Description of Reaction Thermochemistry

type of process	examples	minimum level of calculation required
no conservation of number of electron pairs	homolytic bond dissociation, absolute activation energies	correlated methods including density functional methods; large basis sets
conservation of number of electron pairs but no conservation of number of electron pair bonds	heterolytic bond dissociation	Hartree-Fock methods; moderate to large basis sets
conservation of total number of electron pair bonds but no conservation of number of each kind of bond	hydrogenation, structural isomerism	Hartree-Fock methods; moderate to large basis sets
conservation of number of each kind of bond (*isodesmic* reactions)	bond separation, regio and stereochemical comparisons, conformational changes	Hartree-Fock methods; small to moderate basis sets

$$2H_2C = CH_2 \rightarrow H_3C - CH_3 + HC \equiv CH \qquad \text{disproportionation}$$

At the other end of the scale are reactions in which the number of each kind of formal chemical bond (and each kind of non-bonded lone pair) are conserved. Such types of reactions have become known as *isodesmic* (equal bond) reactions. Examples include the processes below:

$$H_3C - C \equiv CH + CH_4 \rightarrow H_3C - CH_3 + HC \equiv CH \qquad \text{bond separation}$$

$$(CH_3)_3NH^+ + NH_3 \rightarrow (CH_3)_3N + NH_4^+ \qquad \text{proton transfer}$$

In addition, all regio- and stereochemical comparisons are *isodesmic* reactions, as are conformational changes. Thus, *isodesmic* processes constitute a large class of reactions of considerable importance.

A great number of examples exist of all these types of reactions. This allows generalizations to be made regarding the performance of various levels of calculation with regard to thermochemical comparisons.[1] We briefly summarize this experience below.

i) Correlated models (including density functional models) with moderate to large basis sets including one or more sets of polarization functions, and perhaps as well diffuse functions, are required for the accurate description of reactions such as homolytic bond dissociation in which the total number of electron pairs is not conserved. Hartree-Fock models and local density functional models, in particular, give unsatisfactory results for homolytic bond dissociation processes. Hartree-Fock models yield bond dissociation energies which are consistently too small while local density functional models yield energies which are too large.

ii) The energetics of reactions in which the total number of electron pairs are conserved, including heterolytic bond dissociation reactions in which a bond is exchanged for a non-bonded lone pair, are generally well described using Hartree-Fock models. Moderate to large basis sets including polarization functions and, in the case of heterolytic bond dissociation reactions in which anions are produced, diffuse functions are required. Correlated models (including density functional models) also perform well for these classes of reactions, although basis sets which are even larger than those needed for Hartree-Fock models may be required.

iii) The energetics of *isodesmic* reactions are generally well described using both Hartree-Fock and correlated (including density functional) methods. Small to moderate basis sets usually give acceptable results for Hartree-Fock models, although larger basis sets are required for use with correlated (including density functional) models.

iv) Semi-empirical models are generally unsatisfactory for the description of the energetics of all classes of reactions. Even *isodesmic* reactions, which are reasonably well described using minimal basis set Hartree-Fock models, are poorly represented. We believe that the primary reason for the failure of semi-empirical methods to account for reaction energetics, even for reactions for which electron correlation effects would be expected to cancel, is that they have been parameterized to minimize absolute errors in heats of formation rather than to minimize errors in reaction energies. Errors in individual heats of formation in present-generation semi-empirical methods are random errors and large enough (~7 kcal/mol in the case of AM1) such that the overall error in a given reaction will be unacceptably large. Future generation semi-empirical methods might be more successful for energetic comparisons were they to be parameterized to reproduce energies for specific classes of reactions.

The primary recommendation to follow from these generalizations (aside from needing to exercise caution in the use of semi-empirical models for energetic comparisons of any kind) is to make use of *isodesmic* reactions wherever possible. Where this is not possible, try to write reactions in which the total number of chemical bonds is conserved.

4.2 Can we use *isodesmic* reactions to obtain heats of formation for use in other types of thermochemical comparisons?

Overall, all levels of calculation (semi-empirical models excluded) perform best for *isodesmic* reactions. For example, the *isodesmic* process relating proton affinities of a variety of nitrogen bases to that of ammonia as a standard (**Table 4-2**) shows the level of agreement between theory and experiment which can be expected. Here it is seen that the HF/6-31G*, B3LYP/6-31G* and MP2/6-31G* models provide excellent descriptions of relative proton affinities. Even the HF/STO-3G scheme is successful, but surprisingly, calculations using the 3-21G basis set provide a less satisfactory account. This is likely do to the unsatisfactory description of the local geometry about nitrogen in the neutral bases (see also **Sections 2.9** and **2.12**). Note also, that local density functional (SVWN/6-31G*) calculations do not provide a completely satisfactory account of relative proton affinities. In particular, the proton affinity of aniline is greatly in error. Not unexpected is the poor performance of the AM1 model. Numerous other examples available elsewhere show similar trends.[1]

As commented in the previous section, it is advantageous to construct all energetic comparisons in terms of *isodesmic* processes. While it is obvious how to do this for comparisons which involve relative quantities, e.g., nitrogen basicities relative to ammonia, it is less evident how to construct *isodesmic* reactions to describe other types of comparisons. The question really is whatever *isodesmic* reactions are restricted to "novelty applications", or whether they can be applied in a more general context. We examine here use of calculated energies for a special case of *isodesmic reactions*, termed bond separation reactions, together with experimental thermochemical data, to provide heats of formation. Once obtained in this manner, these may then be employed in whatever types of thermochemical comparisons as needed.

A bond separation reaction is a reaction which "breaks down" any molecule comprising three or more heavy (non-hydrogen) atoms, and which can be represented in terms of a classical valence structure, into the simplest set of two-heavy-atom molecules containing the same component bonds. It is

Table 4-2: Calculated Proton Affinities of Nitrogen Bases Relative to Ammonia[a]

nitrogen base	AM1	STO-3G	3-21G	6-31G*	SVWN/ 6-31G*	B3LYP/ 6-31G*	MP2/ 6-31G*	expt.
nitrogen	−65	−118	−101	−99	−95	−96	−91	−94
acetonitrile	−19	−38	−28	−23	−23	−23	−23	−17
methyleneimine	0	−1	4	5	−2	1	2	−3
ammonia	0	0	0	0	0	0	0	0
aniline	3	8	1	8	0	6	—	7
methylamine	2	9	17	11	8	10	11	9
aziridine	3	9	13	14	8	11	11	10
ethylamine	4	13	17	14	11	13	14	12
pyridine	8	18	21	18	13	16	—	15
dimethylamine	3	15	14	18	13	16	18	16
trimethylamine	4	20	10	22	14	19	22	19
quinuclidine	12	31	31	33	25	30	—	30

a) Energies (enthalpies) of reactions: $BH^+ + NH_3 \rightarrow B + NH_4^+$.

a unique attribute of the molecule, or more precisely, a unique attribute of a given valence description of the molecule. This is, of course, an advantage but it is also a liability, as it forces description in terms of a single conventional valence structure. Because we will not always be able to write unique valence structures, we will not always be able to construct unique bond separation reactions, but this is the exception, not the rule.[2]

A single example illustrates what is involved. The bond separation reaction for methylhydrazine,

$$CH_3NHNH_2 + NH_3 \rightarrow CH_3NH_2 + NH_2NH_2,$$

breaks the molecule into methylamine and hydrazine, the simplest molecules incorporating CN and NN single bonds, respectively. A molecule of ammonia needs to be added to the left to achieve stoichiometric balance.

Even Hartree-Fock models using small to moderate size basis sets generally provide adequate descriptions of the energies of bond separation reactions. Examples are provided in **Table 4-3**. As with the previous *isodesmic* basicity comparisons (**Table 4-2**) results are given for Hartree-Fock models using STO-3G, 3-21G$^{(*)}$ and 6-31G* basis sets as well as SVWN/6-31G* and B3LYP/6-31G* density functional models and the MP2/6-31G* correlated model. Finally, semi-empirical AM1 bond separation energies are provided.

All Hartree-Fock and correlated (including density functional) models generally yield bond separation energies within 2-4 kcal/mol of the experimental values. Errors from AM1 calculations are much larger. The ability of most of the computational models (including some of the simplest models) to accurately describe the energetics of bond separation reactions, together with the fact that thermochemical data for nearly all molecules which appear on the right of bond separation reactions are known experimentally (or may be determined accurately from high-level calculations), leads to the suggestion that heats of formation may be accurately established by combining theoretical and experimental results. For example, the heat of formation of methylhydrazine may be obtained from the following thermodynamic cycle,

$$\Delta H_f(CH_3NHNH_2) = -\Delta E_{rx} - \Delta H_f(NH_3) + \Delta H_f(CH_3NH_2) + \Delta H_f(NH_2NH_2),$$

where ΔE_{rx} is the calculated energy of the bond separation reaction for methylhydrazine and $\Delta H_f(NH_3)$, $\Delta H_f(CH_3NH_2)$ and $\Delta H_f(NH_2NH_2)$ are experimental heats of formation. Heats of formation determined in this way for a number of simple molecules using HF/6-31G*, SVWN/6-31G* B3LYP/6-31G* and MP2/6-31G* models are compared to experimental values in **Table 4-4**. The errors are in the range of 2-4 kcal/mol (the same as observed for the bond separation energies). Data from lower level Hartree-Fock models would produce similar (but slightly larger errors), while semi-empirical models would lead errors of unacceptable magnitude.

---

2. Delocalized systems are the most problematic, insofar as no single valence structure offers a completely satisfactory description. Ions and free radicals also present problems and transition states are not generally subject to treatment in this manner.

Table 4-3: Energies of Bond Separation Reactions

molecule	bond separation reaction	HF/ AM1	HF/ STO-3G	HF/ 3-21G(*)	SVWN/ 6-31G*	B3LYP/ 6-31G*	MP2/ 6-31G*	6-31G*	expt.
propane	$CH_3CH_2CH_3 + CH_4 \rightarrow 2CH_3CH_3$	-2	1	1	1	2	1	2	3
ethylamine	$CH_3CH_2NH_2 + CH_4 + \rightarrow CH_3CH_3 + CH_3NH_2$	-1	2	3	3	5	4	4	3
dimethylamine	$CH_3NHCH_3 + NH_3 \rightarrow 2CH_3NH_2$	-2	1	2	2	4	3	4	4
trimethylamine	$(CH_3)_3N + 2NH_3 \rightarrow 3CH_3NH_2$	-6	3	6	5	11	7	11	10
trans ethanol	$CH_3CH_2OH + CH_4 \rightarrow CH_3CH_3 + CH_3OH$	-3	3	5	4	6	5	5	5
dimethyl ether	$CH_3OCH_3 + H_2O \rightarrow 2CH_3OH$	-2	1	2	3	5	3	5	4
trans ethanethiol	$CH_3CH_2SH + CH_4 \rightarrow CH_3CH_3 + CH_3SH$	-2	0	2	1	3	2	3	3
dimethyl sulfide	$CH_3SCH_3 + H_2S \rightarrow 2CH_3OH$	-1	1	1	1	3	2	3	2
propene	$CH_3CHCH_2 + CH_4 \rightarrow CH_3CH_3 + CH_2CH_2$	1	5	4	4	7	5	5	5
acetaldehyde	$CH_3CHO + CH_4 \rightarrow CH_3CH_3 + HCCH$	0	8	10	10	13	11	11	11
propyne	$CH_3CCH + CH_4 \rightarrow CH_3CH_3 + HCCH$	3	8	8	8	12	10	8	7
acetonitrile	$CH_3CN + CH_4 \rightarrow CH_3CH_3 + HCN$	3	11	13	12	14	13	11	14

Table 4-3: Energies of Bond Separation Reactions (continued)

molecule	bond separation reaction	HF/ AM1	HF/ STO-3G	HF/ 3-21G(*)	SVWN/ 6-31G*	B3LYP/ 6-31G*	MP2/ 6-31G*	6-31G*	expt.
allene	$CH_2CCH_2 + CH_4 \rightarrow 2CH_2CH_2$	-4	0	-3	-4	4	1	-2	-4
ketene	$CH_2CO + CH_4 \rightarrow CH_2CH_2 + H_2CO$	-1	16	19	14	24	18	17	15
carbon dioxide	$CO_2 + CH_4 \rightarrow 2H_2CO$	26	54	59	61	68	62	66	61
trans 1,3 butadiene	$CH_2CHCHCH_2 + 2CH_4 \rightarrow CH_3CH_3 + 2CH_2CH_2$	3	13	11	11	18	15	14	11
formamide	$NH_2CHO + CH_4 \rightarrow CH_3NH_2 + H_2CO$	15	20	37	31	39	34	33	30
benzene	$+ 6CH_4 \rightarrow 3CH_3CH_3 + CH_2CH_2$	28	70	60	58	73	66	71	64
pyridine	$+ 5CH_4 + NH_3 \rightarrow 2CH_3CH_3 + 2CH_2CH_2 + CH_3NH_2 + CH_2NH$	29	70	71	61	75	68	74	72
cyclopropane	$+ 3CH_4 \rightarrow 3CH_3CH_3$	-44	-45	-31	-26	-30	-25	-24	-22
azacyclopropane	$+ 2CH_4 + NH_3 \rightarrow CH_3CH_3 + 2CH_3NH_2$	-40	-40	-33	-22	-26	-21	-18	-17
oxacyclopropane	$+ 2CH_4 + H_2O \rightarrow CH_3CH_3 + 2CH_3OH$	-46	-35	-31	-20	-22	-17	-13	-14

Table 4-3: Energies of Bond Separation Reactions (continued)

molecule	bond separation reaction	HF/ AM1	HF/ STO-3G	HF/ 3-21G(*)	SVWN/ 6-31G*	B3LYP/ 6-31G*	MP2/ 6-31G*	6-31G*	expt.
thiacylcopropane	$\triangle$S + 2CH$_4$ + H$_2$S $\rightarrow$ CH$_3$CH$_3$ + 2CH$_3$SH	-40	-35	-30	-16	-18	-13	-11	-15
cyclopentadiene	+ 5CH$_4$ $\rightarrow$ 3CH$_3$CH$_3$ + 2CH$_2$CH$_2$	-12	16	11	11	22	17	21	22
thiophene	S + 4CH$_4$ + H$_2$S $\rightarrow$ CH$_3$CH$_3$ + 2CH$_3$SH+ 2CH$_2$CH$_2$	13	41	30	29	45	38	46	29

Table 4-4: Heats of Formation from Bond Separation Reactions

molecule	bond separation reaction	HF/ 6-31G*	SVWN/ 6-31G*	B3LYP/ 6-31G*	MP2/ 6-31G*	expt.
propane	$CH_3CH_2CH_3 + CH_4 \rightarrow 2CH_3CH_3$	-24	-25	-24	-25	-25.0
isobutane	$CH(CH_3)_3 + 2CH_4 \rightarrow 3CH_3CH_3$	-27	-31	-28	-31	-32.1
neopentane	$C(CH_3)_4 + 3CH_4 \rightarrow 4CH_3CH_3$	-31	-39	-32	-39	-40.0
ethylamine	$CH_3CH_2NH_2 + CH_4 \rightarrow CH_3CH_3 + CH_3NH_2$	-11	-13	-12	-12	-11.4
dimethylamine	$CH_3NHCH_3 + NH_3 \rightarrow 2CH_3NH_2$	-2	-4	-3	-4	-4.5
trimethylamine	$(CH_3)_3N + 2NH_3 \rightarrow 3CH_3NH_2$	0	-6	-2	-6	-5.7
trans ethanol	$CH_3CH_2OH + CH_4 \rightarrow CH_3CH_3 + CH_3OH$	-54	-56	-55	-55	-56.1
dimethyl ether	$CH_3OCH_3 + H_2O \rightarrow 2CH_3OH$	-41	-43	-41	-43	-44.0
trans ethanethiol	$CH_3CH_2SH + CH_4 \rightarrow CH_3CH_3 + CH_3SH$	-9	-11	-10	-11	-11.1
dimethyl sulfide	$CH_3SCH_3 + H_2S \rightarrow 2CH_3SH$	-7	-8	-8	-9	-9.0
difluoromethane	$CH_2F_2 + CH_4 \rightarrow 2CH_3F$	-106	-110	-107	-108	-106.8
trifluoromethane	$CHF_3 + 2CH_4 \rightarrow 3CH_3F$	-165	-176	-167	-170	-164.5
tetrafluoromethane	$CF_4 + 3CH_4 \rightarrow 4CH_3F$	-225	-242	-227	-231	-221
dichloromethane	$CH_2Cl_2 + CH_4 \rightarrow 2CH_3Cl$	-20	-25	-23	-24	-22.1
trichloromethane	$CHCl_3 + 2CH_4 \rightarrow 3CH_3Cl$	-14	-26	-20	-23	-24.7
tetrachloromethane	$CCl_4 + 3CH_4 \rightarrow 4CH_3Cl$	0	-24	-13	—	-25.6

Table 4-4: Heats of Formation from Bond Separation Reactions (continued)

molecule	bond separation reaction	HF/ 6-31G*	SVWN/ 6-31G*	B3LYP/ 6-31G*	MP2/ 6-31G*	expt.
propene	$CH_3CHCH_2 + CH_4 \rightarrow CH_3CH_3 + CH_2CH_2$	6	3	5	5	4.8
acetaldehyde	$CH_3CHO + CH_4 \rightarrow CH_3CH_3 + H_2CO$	−40	−43	−41	−41	−39.6
propyne	$CH_3CCH + CH_4 \rightarrow CH_3CH_3 + HCCH$	44	40	42	44	44.6
acetonitrile	$CH_3CN + CH_4 \rightarrow CH_3CH_3 + HCN$	18	17	17	19	15.4
allene	$CH_2CCH_2 + CH_4 \rightarrow 2CH_2CH_2$	47	38	42	45	45.6
ketene	$CH_2CO + CH_4 \rightarrow CH_2CH_2 + H_2CO$	−11	−21	−15	−14	−11.4
carbon dioxide	$CO_2 + CH_4 \rightarrow 2H_2CO$	−99	−106	−100	−104	−94.0
trans 1,3-butadiene	$CH_2CHCHCH_2 + 2CH_4 \rightarrow CH_3CH_3 + 2CH_2CH_2$	29	22	25	26	26.3
formamide	$NH_2CHO + CH_4 \rightarrow CH_3NH_2 + H_2CO$	−46	−54	−49	−48	−44.5
benzene	+ $6CH_4 \rightarrow 3CH_3CH_3 + 3CH_2CH_2$	26	11	17	13	19.8
pyridine	+ $5CH_4 + NH_3 \rightarrow 2CH_3CH_3 + 2CH_2CH_2 + CH_3NH_2 + CH_2NH$	44	30	37	31	33.8

Table 4-4: Heats of Formation from Bond Separation Reactions (continued)

molecule	bond separation reaction	HF/ 6-31G*	SVWN/ 6-31G*	B3LYP/ 6-31G*	MP2/ 6-31G*	expt.
pyridazine	+ 4CH$_4$ + 2NH$_3$ → 2CH$_3$CH$_3$ + CH$_2$CH$_2$ + 2CH$_2$NH + NH$_2$NH$_2$	99	85	91	84	66.5
pyrimidine	+ 4CH$_4$ + 2NH$_3$ → CH$_3$CH$_3$ + CH$_2$CH$_2$ + 2CH$_3$NH$_2$ + 2CH$_2$NH	61	49	55	49	47.0
pyrazine	+ 4CH$_4$ + 2NH$_3$ → CH$_3$CH$_3$ + CH$_2$CH$_2$ + 2CH$_3$NH$_2$ + 2CH$_2$NH	67	52	59	52	46.8
cyclopropane	+ 3CH$_4$ → 3CH$_3$CH$_3$	19	23	18	17	12.7
azacyclopropane	+ 2CH$_4$ + NH$_3$ → CH$_3$CH$_3$ + 2CH$_3$NH$_2$	37	41	36	33	30.2
oxacyclopropane	+ 2CH$_4$ + H$_2$O → CH$_3$CH$_3$ + 2CH$_3$OH	–2	–1	–6	–10	–12.6
thiacyclopropane	+ 2CH$_4$ + H$_2$S → CH$_3$CH$_3$ + 2CH$_3$SH	25	27	22	20	19.6
cyclobutane	+ 4CH$_4$ → 4CH$_3$CH$_3$	14	14	12	9	6.8
cyclopropene	+ 3CH$_4$ → 2CH$_3$CH$_3$ + CH$_2$CH$_2$	76	76	71	70	66.2

Table 4-4: Heats of Formation from Bond Separation Reactions (continued)

molecule	bond separation reaction	HF/ 6-31G*	SVWN/ 6-31G*	B3LYP/ 6-31G*	MP2/ 6-31G*	expt.
cyclobutene	$+ 4CH_4 \rightarrow 3CH_3CH_3 + CH_2CH_2$	47	43	43	41	37.5
cyclopentadiene	$+ 5CH_4 \rightarrow 3CH_3CH_3 + 2CH_2CH_2$	42	31	36	32	31.3
thiophene	$+ 4CH_4 + H_2S \rightarrow CH_3CH_3 + 2CH_3SH + 2CH_2CH_2$	41	25	32	24	27.5
methylenecyclopropane	$+ 4CH_4 \rightarrow 3CH_3CH_3 + CH_2CH_2$	54	52	50	50	47.9
bicyclo[1.1.0]butane	$+ 6CH_4 \rightarrow 5CH_3CH_3$	54	58	50	46	51.9

The overall recommendation is clear. Wherever possible (where unique valence structures can be drawn) obtain thermochemical data using isodesmic reactions, and then use these data for whatever purposes as needed.[3]

4.3 Do theoretical models which account explicitly for electron correlation always provide more accurate descriptions of reaction thermochemistry than Hartree-Fock models which do not?

This question is important because of a strong tendency to assume that higher levels of calculation will always give results which are superior to those from lower levels. While this is certainly the case in the limit of full treatment of electron correlation and complete basis set, for practical applications the answer depends both on the specific thermochemical comparison at hand and on the details of the theoretical model. A similar question, with regard to equilibrium geometry has already been posed in **Section 2.8**.

As pointed out in **Section 4.1**, proper description of the thermochemistry of reactions where reactants and products incorporate different numbers of electron pairs, e.g., homolytic bond dissociation reactions, requires models which take account of electron correlation. Hartree-Fock and local density functional schemes are completely unreliable, but so too are correlated methods without medium to large basis sets which include polarization type functions.

The more interesting situation involves reactions for which the total number of electron pairs is conserved. These include reactions such as heterolytic bond dissociation reactions, where bonds are swapped for lone pairs, and of greater importance, reactions which conserve the total number of bonds, but do not conserve the numbers of each kind of bond. Finally, they include *isodesmic* reactions which balance the number of each kind of bond. In all of these cases, one might hope for partial cancellation of electron correlation effects, and the success of Hartree-Fock models in providing reasonable thermochemical descriptions. The question which then needs to be answered is whether or not in these cases correlated models offer significant advantages over simpler Hartree-Fock schemes.

Hydrogenation energies calculated for a few simple molecules using Hartree-Fock, SVWN and B3LYP density functional and MP2 correlated models with a variety of basis sets ranging from simple split-valence to one which the valence description is triply split and includes multiple sets of polarization functions are provided in **Table 4-5**. Additional examples with these same models but restricted to the 6-31G* basis set have already been provided in **Table 2-13**. Many further data have been presented and discussed elsewhere.[1]

Hydrogenation energies obtained with the 3-21G basis set are not reliable for any of the models. While some comparisons at this level are actually very good, others are greatly in error. At the other extreme, all models except the SVWN model perform quite well when used in conjunction with the 6-311+G(2d,p) basis set. In particular, hydrogenation energies are typically in error by only a few kcal/mol at the HF/6-311+G(2d,p) level, although in one

---

3. Future versions of SPARTAN will attempt to automatically furnish a valence structure for the molecule at hand and based on this structure provide an estimated heat of formation.

Table 4-5: Energies of Hydrogenation Reactions

reaction	model	3-21G	6-31G*	6-311+ G(2d,p)	expt.
$CH_3CH_3 + H_2 \rightarrow 2CH_4$	HF	−25	−22	−21	−19
	SVWN	−17	−17	−17	
	B3LYP	−20	−19	−20	
	MP2	−18	−16	−19	
$CH_3F + H_2 \rightarrow CH_4 + HF$	HF	−22	−23	−29	−29
	SVWN	−12	−19	−29	
	B3LYP	−12	−18	−28	
	MP2	−16	−21	−31	
$F_2 + H_2 \rightarrow 2HF$	HF	−98	−126	−145	−133
	SVWN	−74	−106	−134	
	B3LYP	−73	−105	−131	
	MP2	−79	−116	−140	
$CH_2{=}CH_2 + 2H_2 \rightarrow 2CH_4$	HF	−71	−66	−61	−57
	SVWN	−71	−70	−67	
	B3LYP	−63	−62	−58	
	MP2	−56	−58	−59	
$N \equiv N + 3H_2 \rightarrow 2NH_3$	HF	−53	−28	−34	−37
	SVWN	−57	−55	−68	
	B3LYP	−34	−28	−41	
	MP2	−5	−13	−31	

case (hydrogenation of fluorine) the error is much greater. The success of "limiting" Hartree-Fock models suggests that correlation effects are not of great importance in describing the energetics of hydrogenation, in other words, that higher-order schemes which explicitly treat correlation are really not required.

While SVWN/6-311+G(2d,p) hydrogenation energies are in reasonable accord with experimental data for saturated molecules, they are in very poor agreement for the unsaturated systems included in the table. The reason for the failure is unclear but parallels other known shortcomings of SVWN models for energetic comparisons.

The 6-311+G(2d,p) basis set is too large to be generally applicable for comparisons of this kind (at least at present), and we need to look for less costly alternatives. Calculations using the popular 6-31G* polarization basis set are one such possibility. In most cases, the Hartree-Fock results are quite close to their "limiting" (HF/6-311+G(2d,p)) values, while those obtained from the SVWN/6-31G*, B3LYP/6-31G* or MP2/6-31G* models are in less satisfactory agreement. These results imply that correlated descriptions converge more slowly than Hartree-Fock descriptions, and suggest that the latter may actually provide better results for basis sets which are small enough to (presently) be of practical value.

Relative energies for a few pairs of structural isomers evaluated using the same set of models are given in **Table 4-6**. Further comparison using the same models but restricted to the 6-31G* basis set have already been provided in **Table 2-14**, and a much larger set of comparisons provided elsewhere.[1]

The 3-21G basis set is somewhat less reliable than the two larger representations although, except for comparisons involving highly-strained systems, the differences are not great. Generally speaking, all models coupled with either the 6-31G* or 6-311+G(2d,p) basis set provide a credible account of isomer energy. The success of Hartree-Fock schemes again points to a high degree of cancellation of correlation effects, and suggests their utility in this regard.

The SVWN and B3LYP density functional models incorrectly assign allene as more stable than propyne, irrespective of basis set. This has yet to be explained adequately. Caution is urged in applications which might involve comparisons of this kind. The SVWN model also does not provide a good description of the relative energies of saturated cyclic and unsaturated acyclic isomers, in particular, 1,3-butadiene vs. bicyclo[1.1.0]butane. Again the reason is unclear.

Energies for a small selection of *isodesmic* reactions obtained from the various models are provided in **Table 4-7**. A larger selection of examples with the same models but restricted to the 6-31G* basis set have previously been provided in **Table 2-15**. Hartree-Fock models even with the 3-21G[*] basis set do a respectable job, although larger representations are needed for correlated (including density functional) models. In the "limit" (6-311+G(2d,p) basis set) all methods provide an acceptable account.

Overall, the limited comparisons presented here and the much larger number of comparisons available elsewhere[1] strongly suggest that there is little gain (and perhaps some loss) from the application of models which take explicit account of electron correlation to the description of the energetics of reactions

Table 4-6: Relative Energies of Structural Isomers

more stable/ less stable isomer	model	3-21G	6-31G*	6-311+ G(2d,p)	expt.
acetonitrile/methyl isocyanide	HF	20.5	24.1	20.7	20.9
	SVWN	28.7	25.3	25.3	
	B3LYP	20.8	26.7	24.0	
	MP2	31.4	28.5	27.0	
acetaldehyde/oxacyclo– propane	HF	34.2	30.5	32.1	26.2
	SVWN	29.2	21.5	22.7	
	B3LYP	32.4	27.5	28.0	
	MP2	35.9	27.2	28.4	
ethylamine/dimethylamine	HF	5.8	5.5	7.5	6.9
	SVWN	4.5	4.8	7.7	
	B3LYP	4.7	4.9	7.6	
	MP2	6.2	6.4	8.0	
propyne/allene	HF	3.4	2.0	2.0	1.6
	SVWN	–2.1	–4.3	–3.2	
	B3LYP	–0.5	–2.7	–1.9	
	MP2	8.5	4.8	5.0	
acetone/propionaldehyde	HF	6.2	7.4	7.5	6.5
	SVWN	9.1	8.8	8.8	
	B3LYP	7.9	7.7	7.8	
	MP2	7.4	7.6	6.6	
1,3-butadiene/bicyclo– [1.1.0] butane	HF	45.7	30.0	34.8	23.1
	SVWN	26.1	12.6	16.1	
	B3LYP	39.9	27.6	31.8	
	MP2	42.6	20.5	25.5	

Table 4-7: Energies of Isodesmic Reactions

reaction	model	3-21G$^{(*)}$	6-31G*	6-311+ G(2d,p)	expt.
$CH_3OCH_3 + H_2O \rightarrow 2CH_3OH$	HF	2	3	3	4.4
	SVWN	2	5	5	
	B3LYP	1	3	3	
	MP2	3	5	5	
$CH_3C \equiv N + CH_4 \rightarrow CH_3CH_3 + HCN$	HF	13	12	12	14.4
	SVWN	15	14	14	
	B3LYP	13	13	12	
	MP2	11	11	11	
△ + $3CH_4 \rightarrow 3CH_3CH_3$	HF	–31	–26	–25	–22.1
	SVWN	–37	–30	–28	
	B3LYP	–32	–26	–23	
	MP2	–30	–24	–24	
⊿S + $2CH_4 + H_2S \rightarrow$ $CH_3CH_3 + 2CH_3SH$	HF	–20	–16	–15	–14.9
	SVWN	–23	–18	–17	
	B3LYP	–18	–13	–12	
	MP2	–16	–11	–11	
$(CH_3)_3NH^+ + NH_3 \rightarrow (CH_3)_3N + NH_4^+$	HF	21	22	25	19.0
	SVWN	9	14	18	
	B3LYP	15	19	23	
	MP2	17	19	22	

where correlation effects largely cancel. In fact, only when very large basis sets are employed are the results from density functional and MP2 correlated models as close to experiment as those from simpler Hartree-Fock schemes.

We need to emphasize that with sophisticated correlation treatment and very large basis sets, calculations are capable of providing much more accurate thermochemical data than available from the limited models discussed here. Indeed, with "all the stops pulled out", calculations are quite able to provide information as accurate as that from experiment. The point we want to make is that many thermochemical comparisons can be formulated to take advantage of cancellation of errors, and that in these situations even modest methods may lead to acceptable results.

5

Making Use of Energy Data for Kinetic Comparisons

Transition state theory relates activation energy to overall reaction rate; the smaller the activation energy the faster the reaction. Knowledge of absolute rate is certainly required in some situations, for example, to estimate temperature and pressure conditions required for a given transformation, or to assess the importance of different reactions competing for the same reactant. In other situations, however, knowledge of relative reaction rates will suffice. One very important example is in the elucidation of product regio- and/or stereochemistry, which involves comparison of rates of closely-related processes.

Experience with thermochemical comparisons (see **Chapter 4**), suggests that absolute activation energies (leading to absolute rates) will be more difficult to obtain accurately from calculation than relative activation energies (leading to relative rates). We examine this in more detail in **Section 5.1**. **Section 5.2** parallels our earlier treatment of *isodesmic* reactions in dealing with thermochemical comparisons (**Section 4.2**), and attempts to formulate strategies by which low-level theoretical models will be able to properly account for relative activation energies. Finally, a brief discussion of solvent effects on reaction thermodynamics, transition state energies and on reaction profiles in general is provided in **Section 5.3**.

5.1 What levels of calculation are required for accurate descriptions of absolute activation energies?

This question is closely related to that posed in the previous chapter regarding the use of energy data for thermochemical comparisons. The common wisdom is that accurate description of activation energies for organic reactions requires the use of correlated methods with underlying polarization basis sets. The reasoning is that transition states will involve varying degrees of bond making and bond breaking and, at least for some classes of reactions, it is likely that the total number of electron pairs will not be the same as in the reactant. It might also be anticipated that present-generation semi-empirical models will not fare very well in their description of absolute activation energies, simply because transition state energetics was not taken explicitly into account in their parameterization.

The data in **Table 5-1** confirm these expectations, at least to the extent that they show that activation energies depend strongly on the level of calculation. Hartree-Fock activation energies generally show sensitivity to basis set, and are typically larger than experimental values; the correlated MP2 model generally leads to a significant lowering of activation barriers. The latter results are paralleled by those from density functional models (not provided here but already discussed in **Section 3.8**), the exception being local density functional models which are well known to greatly underestimate activation energies, in some cases even resulting in "transition states" which are lower in energy than the corresponding reactants. The performance of semi-empirical methods is highly variable. All in all, it does not appear that proper description of absolute activation energies is an easy objective.

Again it needs to be emphasized that much more sophisticated models than those dealt with here are available for the description of the absolute activation energies. As in the case of reaction thermochemistry (see **Section 4.3**), calculations are now available of supply data as accurate and as reliable as that available from experiment. Our present focus is on methods which can be routinely applied to "real reactions", and the models we have considered represent practical limits given present technology.

5.2 What is the best way to use energy data from low-level calculations for kinetic comparisons?

While knowledge of absolute activation energies is certainly important in some situations, there are numerous other situations where it is not. For example, proper accounting of remote substituent effects or regio- and/or stereo product distributions does not require knowledge of absolute activation energies but only accurate relative activation energies. This turns out to be a much simpler task, and one for which even relatively simple (and practical) levels of calculation are properly suited. Three sets of examples illustrate the point. The first (**Table 5-2**) compares calculated and experimental activation energies for Diels-Alder cycloadditions of a variety of cyanoethylenes with cyclopentadiene, relative to the addition of acrylonitrile with cyclopentadiene as a standard, i.e.,

Table 5-1: Activation Energies of Organic Reactions

reaction	AM1	STO-3G	3-21G$^{(*)}$	6-31G*	MP2/ 6-31G*	expt.
$CH_3NC \rightarrow CH_3CN$	83	56	58	46	43	38
$HCO_2CH_2CH_3 \rightarrow HCO_2H + C_2H_4$	64	96	62	70	60	40, 44
Cope rearrangement (1,5-hexadiene)	37	56	45	56		36
Claisen rearrangement (allyl, vinyl ether)	32	50	41	48		31
$CF_2 + C_2H_4 \rightarrow CF_2CH_2CH_2$	17	23	27	31	12	
Diels-Alder (cyclopentadiene + ethylene)	28	35	30	40		20
Ene reaction (1-pentene)	67	106	75	84	60	
dipolar cycloaddition (formonitrile oxide + acetylene)	22	21	25	35	8	
$HBF_2 + C_2H_4 \rightarrow CH_3CH_2BF_2$	50	46	35	39	20	
pyranone $\rightarrow$ butadiene + CO_2	62	108	59	60		
sulfolene $\rightarrow$ butadiene + SO_2	43	66	49	49		
$(CH_3)_2N^+CH_2CH_3 \rightarrow (CH_3)_2NOH + C_2H_4$	38	26	36	45		

Table 5-1: Activation Energies of Organic Reactions (continued)

reaction	AM1	STO-3G	3-21G(*)	6-31G*	MP2/6-31G*	expt.
SOH → HOS	24	14	24	33	17	
suprafacial 1,5 hydrogen migration (1,3-pentadiene)	83	62	52	56	35	
antarafacial 1,7 hydrogen migration (1,3,5-heptatriene)	30	48	37	43		

Table 5-2: Relative Activation Energies of Diels-Alder Cycloadditions of Cyclopentadiene with Electron-Deficient Dienophiles

dienophile	stereochemistry of adduct	AM1	STO-3G	3-21G	6-31G*	expt.
ethylene		0	2	4	4	8.5
acrylonitrile	*endo*	1	0	0	0	0
	exo	0	0	0	0	0
trans-1,2-dicyanoethylene		1	−1	−4	−3	−2.6
cis-1,2-dicyanoethylene	*endo*	2	0	−3	−3	−3.8
	exo	1	0	−4	−3	−3.8
1,1-dicyanoethylene		−1	−5	−7	−8	−7.2
tricyanoethylene	*endo*	1	−4	−8	−9	−9.2
	exo	1	−3	−9	−9	−9.2
tetracyanoethylene		2	−4	−11	−11	−11.2

or

where [ ]* denotes the transition state for the reaction. This is an *isodesmic* reaction, and previous experience with equilibrium processes (see **Chapter 4**) suggests that its energy should be relatively well accounted for even with Hartree-Fock models using moderate size basis sets. The data in the table concur. Except for the addition involving ethylene as a dienophile, both HF/3-21G and HF/6-31G* models accurately reproduce the experimental relative activation energies. Both the *ab initio* STO-3G model and the semiempirical AM1 model do not provide accurate accounts. This parallels previous experience in dealing with the thermochemistry of *isodesmic* processes (see **Section 4.2**).

Regio and stereochemical preferences may also be expressed as *isodesmic* processes. For example, the regioselectivity of (*endo*) addition of 2-methylcyclopentadiene with acrylonitrile,

comes down to the energy difference between the transition states leading to *meta* and *para* products, respectively, i.e.,

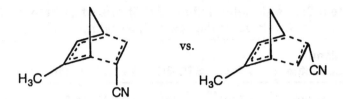

Similarly, the difference in energy between *syn* and *anti* transition states for (*endo*) addition of 5-methylcyclopentadiene with acrylonitrile,

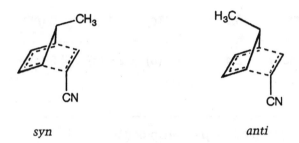

syn	*anti*

provides the difference in stereochemistry for this reaction. Both of these types of comparisons are *isodesmic*; the number of bonds of each formal type are maintained and only the detailed environment has altered.

Table 5-3 summarizes results for regioselectivity in cycloadditions of 1- and 2-substitututed cyclopentadienes with acrylonitrile. All levels of calculations including semi-empirical AM1 and minimal basis set STO-3G levels, qualitatively reproduce what is known experimentally.[1]

A similar conclusion applies to results for facial stereochemistry in cycloadditions of 5-substituted cyclopentadienes with acrylonitrile (Table 5-4). The differences are somewhat larger here than previously noted for regioselectivity.

While our sample is too small to generalize, the conclusion seems to be that low-level Hartree-Fock methods and, in the case of regio- and stereoselection, semi-empirical methods appear to provide a reasonable account of relative activation energies. This is actually quite important (assuming it holds up to further scrutiny) for it means that practical electronic structure techniques may be of considerable value in anticipating product distributions in complex organic reactions.

5.3 To what extent does solvent effect the energetics of gas-phase reactions?

This is another question which we are not yet equipped to answer in a general manner. Rather, we provide only a single example to illustrate in the extreme the effects which solvent may have on the energetics of a gas-phase process.

---

1. Actually, the *ab initio* calculations reproduce three facts about the regiochemistry of Diels-Alder cycloadditions: i) 1-substituted dienes lead preferentially to *ortho* products and 2-substituted dienes to *para* products, ii) methoxy (the better electron donor substituent) leads to higher regioselectivity than methyl for both 1- and 2-substitution, and iii) that substituents in the 1-position are better regiodirectors than the same substituents in the 2-position. The AM1 calculations reproduce the first two experimental observations but not the third.

Table 5-3: Regioselectivity in Additions of Substituted Cyclopentadienes with Acrylonitrile[a]

diene substituent	AM1	STO-3G	3-21G	6-31G*	expt.
1-methyl	0.7 (*o*)	1.0 (*o*)	0.9 (*o*)	1.3 (*o*)	*o*
1-methoxy	1.9 (*o*)	2.7 (*o*)	3.3 (*o*)	4.2 (*o*)	*o*
2-methyl	0.9 (*p*)	0.6 (*p*)	0.1 (*p*)	0.6 (*p*)	*p*
2-methoxy	2.4 (*p*)	2.5 (*p*)	2.9 (*p*)	4.0 (*p*)	*p*

a) *o* = *ortho* product; *p* = *para* product.

Table 5-4: Syn-Anti Selectivity in Additions of 5-Substituted Cyclopentadienes with Electron-Deficient Dienophiles[a]

diene substituent	dienophile	AM1	STO-3G	3-21G(*)	6-31G*	expt.
CH_3	ethylene	2.0 (a)	3.0 (a)	2.5 (a)	0.8 (a)	a
	acrylonitrile	2.0 (a)	3.1 (a)	2.5 (a)	1.1 (a)	a
	cis-1,2-dicyanoethylene	1.9 (a)	3.2 (a)	2.5 (a)	1.2 (a)	a
	tetracyanoethylene	5.5 (a)	6.9 (a)	7.4 (a)	5.6 (a)	a
Cl	ethylene	1.7 (a)	1.8 (a)	0.3 (a)	0.5 (s)	
	acrylonitrile	1.2 (a)	0.9 (a)	1.1 (s)	1.5 (s)	
	cis-1,2-dicyanoethylene	0.7 (a)	0.0	2.2 (s)	2.4 (s)	
	tetracyanoethylene	3.3 (a)	5.3 (a)	5.4 (a)	5.0 (a)	

a) s = *syn* addition; a = *anti* addition.

The S_N2 reaction is perhaps the single most familiar mechanism in all of organic chemistry. It involves approach of a nucleophile ($Nu:^-$) to a tetrahedral carbon opposite to some leaving group (X^-). This geometry allows transfer of lone pair electrons on the nucleophile into an unoccupied σ^* orbital localized on the CX bond. Substitution occurs with the inversion of configuration at carbon and via a trigonal bipyramidal transition state in which bonds to both the incoming nucleophile and outgoing X group are greatly elongated over normal single-bond values.

The prevailing view is that S_N2 displacement occurs in one step, that is, without formation of any intermediates.

While this may be the case in solution, it is certainly not how the reaction occurs in the gas phase, at least where the incoming nucleophile is charged. Here the overall reaction profile involves (at least) two stable ion-molecule complexes (intermediates), one between the incoming nucleophile and the reactant, and the other between the leaving group and the product.

In fact, approach of a changed nucleophile to a neutral reagent is energetically *downhill* in the gas phase, and any barrier to S_N2 displacement in solution is a solvent effect. Charges on both the nucleophile and the leaving group are much more highly localized than the charge on the transition state, and therefore are much better stabilized by solvent

While this particular case is certainly extreme, it does make the point that solvent can be important, not only on the quantitative details of a reaction mechanism, but in dramatically altering the energetic profile. Much further experience will need to be gathered in order to provide generalizations.

6

Dealing with Conformationally Flexible Molecules

Perhaps the greatest obstacle inhibiting the widespread application of electronic structure methods to organic chemistry is treatment of conformationally-flexible molecules. The problem is multifaceted. At the outset, there is the issue of identifying which conformers are actually important. While it might seem obvious that this is the lowest-energy conformer (the global minimum) or the few lowest-energy conformers, a single example should suffice to indicate that this is not always the case. Consider the Diels-Alder cycloaddition of 1,3-butadiene with acrylonitrile.

The diene exists primarily in a *trans* conformation, the *cis* form being approximately 2 kcal/mol less stable and separated from the *trans* by a low barrier. Clearly, *trans* butadiene is unable to undergo Diels-Alder cycloaddition (as a diene), at least via the concerted pathway which is known to occur, and rotation into a *cis* conformation is required before reaction can proceed. Certainly this situation will also occur for other reactions, for which identification of the global minimum will be of little value. The general problem of deciding which conformer (or set of conformers) is actually important to a given situation is discussed briefly in **Section 6.1**.

Following identification of which conformers are actually relevant, we need to develop tactics for actually locating them. **Section 6.2** offers some general comments about location of the global minimum, and briefly describes some of the available procedures for this purpose. **Section 6.3** asks whether practical correlated models, including density functional models, always provide more accurate descriptions of conformational energy differences and rotation/inversion barriers than Hartree-Fock models which do not. The next two sections address the possibility of using approximate geometries (from semi-empirical or low-level *ab initio* models) for conformational studies. The discussion in **Section 6.4** asks to what extent low-level models provide suitable geometries for use in calculations of both conformational energy differences and rotation/inversion barriers in simple systems, i.e., those where the identities of the conformers are apparent. Here, for the first time in this book, we examine the performance of molecular mechanics models, admitting just how difficult the problem of thorough conformational searching really is. **Section 6.5** addresses a more difficult (and more difficult to assess) problem, mainly the differences among various levels of calculation in ordering conformer energies. **Section 6.6** addresses the difficult but quite important question of whether or not different levels of computation yield qualitatively similar descriptions of conformer stabilities. Success of low-level models at least in identifying "good conformers" would be very valuable, and we need to set guidelines as to what is and what is not acceptable performance. **Section 6.7** considers the influence solvent in altering gas-phase conformational energies. This closely parallels the discussion in **Chapter 2 (Section 2.13)**. **Section 6.8** examines the small amount of reliable experimental data available on conformational energy differences for reaction transition states, and tries to reach some general conclusion regarding the performance of simple models to reproduce this data. Finally in **Section 6.9**, we provide a framework for representation of conformational energy profiles suitable for incorporation into empirical molecular mechanics/molecular dynamics schemes.

6.1 Do we always require the lowest-energy conformer or are there situations where higher-energy conformers are more appropriate?

The equilibrium abundance of conformational forms depends strictly on their relative energies. The lowest-energy conformer (global minimum) will be present in the greatest amount, the second lowest energy conformer in the next greatest amount, and so forth. This implies that reactions under **thermodynamic control** and involving conformationally flexible reagents need to be described in terms of the properties of global minima, or more precisely in terms of the properties of all minima weighted by their relative Boltzmann populations.

The situation may be different for reactions under kinetic control, and the lowest-energy conformer(s) of the reagent(s) may not be the one(s) involved in the reaction. We have already eluded to the fact that Diels-Alder cycloadditions of 1,3-butadiene need to involve the higher energy *cis* conformer rather than the ground state *trans* form. Less obvious is the observation (from calculation) that Diels-Alder reactions of 1-substituted *cis*-butadienes and acrolein give different regioproducts depending on the conformation of acrolein. Reactions involving the ground state *trans* form of acrolein give a *meta* product (not observed), while reactions involving *cis* acrolein, which is about 2 kcal/mol higher in energy, lead to the observed *ortho* product.

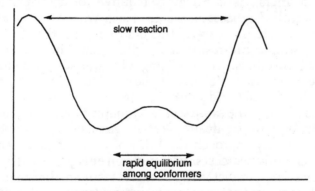

This situation is not as strange as first appearances might convey and fact is a direct consequence the Curtin-Hammett principle.[1] This suggests that the overall activation barrier needs to be based not (necessarily) on the global conformation of the reactant but rather on some "reactive conformation". The latter is perceived to be in rapid equilibrium with the global minimum and, assuming that any barriers which separate these conformations are much smaller than the barrier to reaction (separating the reactive conformer from the product), will be replenished throughout the reaction, i.e.,

In the case of the above mentioned Diels-Alder reactions, *cis* and *trans* acrolein, which differ in energy by about 2 kcal/mol, are separated by an energy barrier which is far smaller than the activation required for cycloaddition. It is not surprising, therefore, that reaction will occur from the higher-energy conformer as this would likely (but not necessarily) lead to a lower overall activation energy.

The above example illustrates only that in kinetically-controlled reactions products do not necessarily derive from the lowest-energy conformer. It does not provide any hint whatsoever about how to identify the "reactive conformer". One reasonable suggestion is that this is the conformer which is

1. (a) D.Y. Curtin, Rec. Chem. Prog., **15**, 111 (1954); (b) L.P. Hammett, **Physical Organic Chemistry**, 2nd ed., McGraw Hill, New York, 1970.

best "poised to react", or alternatively as the conformer which first results from progression backwards along the reaction coordinate starting from the transition state. Operationally, such a conformer is rather easy to identify (far easier than finding the global minimum). All that one needs to do is to start at the transition state and, following a "push" in the direction of reactant, optimize to a stable structure. Given that the transition state may be uniquely defined, the reactive conformer is also uniquely defined.

We offer no "proof" for this simple idea, and only suggest that it appears "to pass" a number of operational tests. One of these is provided in **Table 6-1**.[2] This compares activation energies calculated at the HF/3-21G level for Claisen rearrangements of cyano-substituted allyl vinyl ethers, relative to the unsubstituted compound, with experimentally-derived activation energies. Both global and reactive conformers of reactant have been considered.[3] Overall, the data based on use of the reactive conformation is in better agreement with the experimental relative activation energies than that based on use of the global minima, although except for substitution in the 1-position, the differences are not great. While much further work is needed, there is now clear indication that identifying the global minimum may not be necessary (or more importantly, appropriate) in accounting for reactions under kinetic control.

6.2   What is the best way to locate the lowest-energy conformation?

Once it is decided that it is actually necessary to identify the lowest energy conformer (or more generally to establish the identities and abundances of all low-energy conformers), as is certainly required for description of thermo-dynamically-controlled processes, we are faced with a practical problem of considerable magnitude. To see why this is so, consider the case of conformer generation via a simple grid-research technique, and limited to single bonds not incorporated into rings. Given N single bonds and a grid step of $360°/M$, the number of conformers which need to be considered in such a search is M^N. For three single bonds and a grid step of $120°$ (M=3), this leads to 27 conformers; for five single bonds with the same step, 243 conformers need to be considered. Symmetry may lead to duplicates, but in general the number of unique conformers will closely approach the limit of M^N. For each conformer considered, it will generally be necessary to perform energy minimization in order to relieve severe steric interactions. Also, grid steps smaller than $120°$ may be required in order to avoid missing conformers. Hence, we are dealing with a problem of considerable computational complexity, even for relatively simple flexible acyclic molecules. It becomes even more complex when conformationally flexible rings are involved.

Conformational searching is a very active area of research,[4] and it is well beyond the scope of the present treatment to elaborate in detail or to assess the available strategies. It is worth pointing out that these generally fall into two broad categories:

---

2. W.W. Huang, Ph.D. thesis, University of California, Irvine, 1994.
3. The Claisen rearrangement, like many concerted reactions, proceeds via a "cyclic" transition state. This makes the problem of identifying the lowest energy conformer much easier than for the reactants or products of the reaction.
4. For a review see: A.R. Leach in **Reviews in Computational Chemistry**, K.B. Lipkowitz and D.B. Boyd, eds., vol 2, p.1, VCH Publishers, New York, 1991.

Table 6-1: Activation Energies for Claisen Rearrangements

position of substitution	calculated activation energy		experimental activation energy[a]
	global	reactive	
—	0	0	0
1	−1.0	1.3	1.7
2	−5.8	−3.4	−2.6
4	−2.9	−3.1	−3.1
5	−4.9	−5.2	−2.8
6	2.6	2.3	3.4

a) C.J. Burrows and B.K. Carpenter, J. Am. Chem. Soc., **103**, 6983 (1981).

> i) techniques which do not require energy evaluation, but rely instead on other criteria, e.g., non-bonded contact distances in the case of distance geometry methods, and,

> ii) techniques which explicitly evaluate the energy.

Techniques which do not require explicit energy calculation are obviously much faster than those which do, and have found utility both in surveying systems which are too complex for energy-based methods and for providing lists of "reasonable structures" for later refinement by energy-based methods.

Energy-based techniques which are needed for quantitative assessment, themselves divide into several categories:

> i) torsional driver methods which "walk around" bonds and/or pucker ring centers one at a time,

> ii) Monte-Carlo techniques, which randomly sample conformational space and,

> iii) genetic algorithms which randomly "mutate" populations of conformers in search for "survivors".

There are also hybrid methods which combine features from two or more of the above.

Which technique is the best? Although opinions will freely be offered, the reality is that different techniques will probably perform differently depending on the problem at hand. As with other facets of computational chemistry, a trial-and-error approach is both desirable and to some extent necessary.[5]

A second issue which needs to be addressed for energy-based conformational searching techniques concerns the level of calculation utilized to establish conformation, and following this to evaluate energies and other properties as a function of conformation. This is also an active area of research, and as yet there are not set "recipes". Among the reasonable alternatives are the following:

i) full conformational search using molecular mechanics → geometry optimization using semi-empirical models for selected conformers → single-point calculation or geometry optimization using *ab initio* models for selected conformers

ii) full conformational search using semi-empirical models → single-point calculation or geometry optimization using *ab initio* models for selected conformers

iii) full conformational search using *ab initio* Hartree-Fock or correlated models

Either the first or second alternatives are probably acceptable where the property of interest is the energy, or is directly related to the energy, e.g., proton affinity. In these cases, consideration only of the lowest-energy conformer is

---

5. *SPARTAN* provides all of these techniques.

probably acceptable. Full conformational searching at the *final* level of theory is probably required for the calculation of properties which are not directly related to energy. In these cases, averaging over all low-energy conformers will probably be required.

6.3 Do theoretical models which account explicitly for electron correlation always provide more accurate descriptions of conformational energy differences and barriers to rotation and inversion than Hartree-Fock models which do not?

This question in reminiscent of one previously asked in **Section 4.3** regarding the relative performance of Hartree-Fock and correlated (including density functional) models for a variety of thermochemical comparisons. Here it was noted that, for a wide variety of processes in which the total number of bonds was conserved, correlation effects seemed largely to cancel and there was little reason to use models which took explicit account of the correlation energy. In fact, the slower convergence of correlated methods (relative to Hartree-Fock methods) was given as reason that the latter may actually be preferred in some situations.

Conformational changes, including conformational energy differences and rotation/inversion barriers, are examples of chemical reactions in which the number of bonds is conserved. In fact, they are *isodesmic* processes in that the numbers of each kind of bond are conserved and only the detailed environments are altered. As such, we might expect Hartree-Fock models to provide reasonable descriptions of conformational energy differences. On the other hand, conformational energy differences are apt to be very small, and even very subtle differential correlation effects might be significant. Thus, the case for Hartree-Fock vs. correlated techniques is not at all clear and numerical tests need to be provided.

Table 6-2 summarizes conformational energy differences in a few very simple systems. Hartree-Fock models, SVWN and B3LYP density functional models and the MP2 correlated model have been considered, all with the 6-31G* basis set. In addition, data has been furnished for the smaller systems using the 6-311+G(2d,p) basis set, which while not presently of practical value, probably closely reflects the "limiting behavior" of each of the computational methods.

The HF/6-31G* model appears to provide a reasonable account of conformational energy differences in these systems, although the calculated differences are consistently too large. B3LYP density functional models also provide excellent descriptions; energy differences are both very similar and (usually) smaller than the corresponding Hartree-Fock energy differences. Particularly noteworthy, is the significant reduction in the difference in energies between the *skew* (ground state) and the *cis* conformers of 1-butene, where the Hartree-Fock result was much too large. It is likely that correlation effects are important in "stabilizing" the more crowded *cis* conformer. The SVWN/6-31G* model does not appear to provide as reliable an account of conformational energy differences in this limited class of systems. In particular, the model incorrectly assigns the ground state conformer of 1-butene.

Table 6-2: Conformational Energy Differences

molecule	low energy/ high energy conformer	HF/ 6-31G*	HF/ 6-311+ G(2d,p)	SVWN/ 6-31G*	SVWN/ 6-311+ G(2d,p)	B3LYP/ 6-31G*	B3LYP/ 6-311+ G(2d,p)	MP2/ 6-31G*	MP2/ 6-311+ G(2d,p)	expt.
n-butane	trans/gauche	0.9	1.0	0.4	0.4	0.8	0.8	0.7	0.6	0.77
1-butene	skew/cis	0.7	0.6	-0.8	-0.8	0.4	0.4	0.5	0.3	0.2
1,3-butadiene	trans/gauche	3.0	3.3	3.6	3.5	3.6	3.5	2.6	2.9	1.7, >2, 2.5
acrolein	trans/cis	1.7	2.5	1.7	2.3	1.7	2.3	1.5	2.2	2.0, 2.06
glyoxal	trans/cis	5.6	6.0	4.1	4.6	4.2	4.7	4.3	4.5	3.2
methylcyclohexane	equatorial/axial	2.3	2.5	1.6	1.8	2.1	2.2	1.9	—	1.8
tert-butylcyclohexane	equatorial/axial	6.3	—	4.6	—	5.3	—	—	—	5.4
2-chlorotetrahydropyran	axial/equatorial	2.5	2.5	4.6	4.3	3.7	3.6	2.8	—	1.8

Results using the 6-311+G(2d,p) basis set are generally quite close to those obtained using the smaller 6-31G* representation. We can be confident that the results obtained with the smaller basis set reflect the properties of the limiting methods.

Table 6-3 summarizes single-bond rotation barriers in a few very simple systems. Hartree-Fock models, SVWN and B3LYP density functional models and the MP2 correlated model have been considered, all with the 6-31G* basis set. In addition, data has been furnished using the 6-311+G(2d,p) basis set, which while not presently of practical value, probably closely reflects the "limiting behavior" of each of the computational methods.

At the 6-31G* level, all models provide a good account of rotation barriers in these systems. Errors are typically in the range of a few tenths of a kcal/mol to one kcal/mol. None of the models does particularly better (or worse) than any of the others, leading to the suggestion that there is little benefit to use of correlated schemes for this purpose.

Results from 6-311+G(2d,p) basis calculations are nearly identical to those from the corresponding 6-31G* calculations, suggesting that the energy differences under scrutiny here are subtle enough such that the limit has already been reached with the smaller representation.

Table 6-4 applies the same calculation methods to inversion barriers in a few very simple systems. The range of barriers here is somewhat larger than those for single-bond rotations (**Table 6-3**), and so too are differences between the levels of computation. In general, SVWN/6-31G* and B3LYP/6-31G* models yield inversion barriers which are somewhat smaller than those from both the corresponding Hartree-Fock and correlated MP2 calculations. The largest discrepancy is for inversion in aziridine. Unfortunately, here the experimental data provide only a lower bound and we cannot decide which set of computed barriers is the better.

As in the calculation of conformational energy differences and rotation barriers, use of the 6-311+G(2d,p) basis set produces only small changes.

Overall, the conclusion is that Hartree-Fock schemes provide generally acceptable descriptions of conformational energy differences and rotation/inversion barriers, and that correlation effects are likely small

One final note: If conformer energy differences and/or rotation/inversion barriers can be couched in terms of relative as opposed to absolute quantities, then they are likely to be well described using even very simple levels of calculation. A single example suffices to make the point. **Table 6-5** compares STO-3G and experimental energies for reactions in which the barrier to rotation in a variety of *para* substituted phenols is referenced to phenol.

The agreement is remarkable, and suggests a high level of cancellation.

Table 6-3: Barriers to Rotation

molecule	HF/		SVWN/		B3LYP/		MP2/		expt.
	6-31G*	6-311+G (2d,p)	6-31G*	6-311+G (2d,p)	6-31G*	6-311+G (2d,p)	6-31G*	6-311+G (2d,p)	
BH_3-NH_3	1.9	2.0	2.5	2.5	2.1	2.1	2.1	2.1	3.1
BH_3-PH_3	1.9	2.0	2.9	2.7	2.4	2.3	2.6	2.3	2.5
CH_3-CH_3	3.0	3.0	2.9	2.7	2.8	2.7	3.1	2.9	2.9
CH_3-NH_2	2.4	2.1	2.3	1.9	2.4	1.9	2.6	2.0	2.0
CH_3-OH	1.4	1.1	1.5	1.0	1.4	1.1	1.5	1.1	1.1
CH_3-SiH_3	1.4	1.6	1.5	1.5	1.4	1.0	1.5	1.6	1.7
CH_3-PH_2	2.0	2.0	2.0	1.8	1.9	1.7	2.1	1.9	2.0
CH_3-SH	1.4	1.3	1.4	1.2	1.3	1.1	1.5	1.2	1.3
CH_3-CHO	1.0	1.3	1.2	1.2	1.1	1.1	1.0	1.1	1.2
HO-OH (*cis* barrier)	9.2	8.2	9.6	8.6	8.9	7.9	9.4	8.3	7.0
(*trans* barrier)	0.9	1.3	0.9	1.3	0.7	1.1	0.6	1.1	1.1
HS-SH (*cis* barrier)	8.5	8.3	9.2	8.9	8.2	7.9	8.7	8.1	6.8
(*trans* barrier)	6.1	6.1	6.0	6.2	5.5	5.6	5.9	5.7	6.8

Table 6-4: Barriers to Inversion

molecule	HF/		SVWN/		B3LYP/		MP2/		expt.
	6-31G*	6-311+G(2d,p)	6-31G*	6-311+G(2d,p)	6-31G*	6-311+G(2d,p)	6-31G*	6-311+G(2d,p)	
cyanamide	1.1	1.2	0.4	0.4	0.9	0.8	1.6	1.4	1.9, 2.0
aniline	1.6	—	0.5	—	1.2	—	2.1	—	≈2
methylamine	6.0	5.3	—	—	—	—	6.3	5.2	4.8
ammonia	6.5	5.1	5.2	3.9	6.4	4.7	6.6	5.0	5.8
aziridine	19.4	19.3	15.0	14.7	17.7	16.9	20.2	19.2	>11.6, >12
phosphine	37.8	36.6	33.0	32.4	35.5	34.3	35.4	34.1	31.5

Table 6-5: Substituent Effects on Barriers to Rotation in Phenol[a]

para substituent	STO-3G	expt.
OH	−0.70	−0.87
F	−0.44	−0.60
CH_3	−0.20	−0.30
H	0	0
CN	0.64	0.70
CHO	0.46	0.87
NO_2	0.73	0.98

a) Energies of reactions:

6.4 Do molecular mechanics, semi-empirical and/or low-level *ab initio* models provide an acceptable account of conformational energy differences and barriers to rotation and inversion?

As already commented in **Section 6.2**, searching conformational space represents a formidable computational task, and it is, therefore, desirable to explore the suitability of "inexpensive" methods for this purpose. These include use of parameterized force fields ("molecular mechanics") as well as semi-empirical molecular orbital and small basis set *ab initio* models. We briefly assess the situation using the same set of examples as in the previous section to address the importance of electron correlation effects.

Molecular mechanics procedures were originally formulated to provide accurate descriptions of conformational energy differences in hydrocarbons and, as the data in **Table 6-6** convey, they fare reasonably well in this task. The more "modern" force fields (MM2 and especially MM3) give better results, although even the very simple SYBYL force field performs satisfactorily for saturated systems.

The performance of mechanics schemes for molecules incorporating heteroatoms is less satisfactory. Note, in particular, the failure of SYBYL and MM2 (MM3 parameters are not available) to reproduce the known *axial* preference for 2-chlorotetrahydropyran (the **anomeric effect**).

Molecular mechanics models also generally provide a credible account of rotation (**Table 6-7**) and inversion (**Table 6-8**) barriers.

Semi-empirical models are not entirely satisfactory in their description of conformational energy differences (**Table 6-9**). Except for hydrocarbons, the results from all three models are unreliable. Particularly poorly described are acrolein and glyoxal, where the large stability differences between *cis* and *trans* conformers (the *trans* structures being the more stable) are not reproduced. The same failure is also seen (to a lesser degree) in 1,3-butadiene, where all three semi-empirical models lead to a *trans-gauche* conformer difference of less than half the experimental value.

The surprising poor result for the *equatorial-axial* conformer energy difference in *tert*-butylcyclohexane at the PM3 level warrants special mention. This is illustrative of a more general (and well recognized) problem with PM3, whereby nearby (but non-bonded) hydrogen atoms exhibit significant attraction.

The three semi-empirical models also do not do very well in their description of rotation barriers (**Table 6-10**). Note, in particular, the approximate experimental ratio of the barriers in ethane, methylamine and methanol (3:2:1, reflecting the number of *eclipsing* bonds), is not reproduced. All three models also fail to show a (significant) *trans* barrier in hydrogen peroxide, and a large enough *trans* barrier in hydrogen disulfide.

The performance of semi-empirical models with regard to inversion barriers in nitrogen and phosphorous compounds (**Table 6-11**) is somewhat better. The AM1 model, in particular, performs fairly well, the only significant flaw in the few compounds investigated being the failure to reproduce to known increase in inversion barrier of methylamine over ammonia. Both MNDO and PM3 models tend to provide inversion barriers which are larger than experimental values, sometimes significantly so.

Table 6-6: Conformational Energy Differences

molecule	low energy/ high energy conformer	SYBYL	MM2	MM3	expt.
n-butane	*trans/gauche*	0.6	0.9	0.8	0.77
1-butene	*skew/cis*	1.0	0.5	0.6	0.2
1,3-butadiene	*trans/gauche*	1.0	—	1.4	1.7, >2, 2.5
acrolein	*trans/cis*	0.0	—	1.4	2.0, 2.06
glyoxal	*trans/cis*	0.0	—	—	3.2
methylcyclohexane	*equatorial/axial*	1.4	1.8	1.8	1.8
tert-butylcyclohexane	*equatorial/axial*	7.4	5.5	6.2	5.4
2-chloroterahydropyran	*axial/equatorial*	–0.1	–1.0	—	1.8

Table 6-7: Barriers to Rotation. Molecular Mechanics Models

molecule	SYBYL	MM2	MM3	expt.
BH_3-NH_3	2.2	—	—	3.1
BH_3-PH_3	1.6	—	—	2.5
CH_3-CH_3	3.5	2.5	2.4	2.9
CH_3-NH_2	1.8	1.4	1.5	2.0
CH_3-OH	2.8	0.5	0.6	1.1
CH_3-SiH_3	0.7	1.5	—	1.7
CH_3-PH_2	2.5	1.5	1.4	2.0
CH_3-SH	1.0	—	0.9	1.3
CH_3-CHO	0.0	1.1	0.7	1.2
HO-OH (*cis* barrier)	1.2	3.2	8.0	7.0
(*trans* barrier)	0.0	0.7	1.1	1.1
HS-SH (*cis* barrier)	0.4	—	7.3	6.8
(*trans* barrier)	−0.2	—	5.9	6.8

Table 6-8: Barriers to Inversion

molecule	SYBYL	MM2	MM3	expt.
cyanamide	0.0	—	—	1.9, 2.0
aniline	−0.4	3.0	1.2	≈2
methylamine	0.7	5.5	3.7	4.8
ammonia	0.0	7.9	5.5	5.8
aziridine	53.5	—	—	>11.6, >12
phosphine	0.3	21.1	20.9	31.5

Table 6-9: Conformational Energy Differences: Semi-Empirical Models

molecule	low energy/ high energy conformer	MNDO	AM1	PM3	expt.
n-butane	*trans/gauche*	0.6	0.7	0.5	0.77
1-butene	*skew/cis*	1.3	0.6	1.0	0.2
1,3-butadiene	*trans/gauche*	0.5	0.8	0.7	1.7, >2, 2.5
acrolein	*trans/cis*	0.4	−0.2	0.4	2.0, 2.06
glyoxal	*trans/cis*	1.1	0.0	0.1	3.2
methylcyclohexane	*equatorial/axial*	1.0	1.4	1.1	1.8
tert-butylcyclohexane	*equatorial/axial*	3.9	5.1	1.1	5.4
2-chlorotetrahydropyran	*axial/equatorial*	3.1	3.6	3.1	1.8

Table 6-10: Barriers to Rotation

molecule	MNDO	AM1	PM3	expt.
BH$_3$-NH$_3$	1.0	1.3	—	3.1
BH$_3$-PH$_3$	0.3	0.5	—	2.5
CH$_3$-CH$_3$	1.0	1.3	1.4	2.9
CH$_3$-NH$_2$	1.1	1.3	1.2	2.0
CH$_3$-OH	0.7	1.0	0.9	1.1
CH$_3$-SiH$_3$	0.4	0.4	0.6	1.7
CH$_3$-PH$_2$	0.7	0.8	0.6	2.0
CH$_3$-SH	0.5	0.7	0.7	1.3
CH$_3$-CHO	0.2	0.4	0.6	1.2
HO-OH (*cis* barrier)	6.9	7.0	7.3	7.0
(*trans* barrier)	0.0	0.1	0.0	1.1
HS-SH (*cis* barrier)	5.0	6.1	6.3	6.8
(*trans* barrier)	1.9	2.1	0.2	6.8

Table 6-11: Barriers to Inversion

molecule	MNDO	AM1	PM3	expt.
cyanamide	5.7	1.7	6.0	1.9, 2.0
aniline	4.2	1.0	4.5	≈2
methylamine	7.6	4.2	9.1	4.8
ammonia	11.6	4.2	10.0	5.8
aziridine	20.6	15.7	19.5	>11.6, >12
phosphine	30.0	32.8	22.6	31.5

In summary, present generation semi-empirical molecular orbital methods do not appear well suited to the accurate determination of conformational energy differences and rotation/inversion barriers. They may prove of significant value in identifying conformers in complex systems, but here we will need to rely on other (*ab initio* and/or correlated models) to provide better estimates of relative energies.

STO-3G and 3-21G[*] Hartree-Fock models generally provide a reasonable account of conformational energy differences (**Table 6-12**). All models properly assign the lowest energy conformer and generally yield energy differences which are in reasonable accord with experimental data. Also, energy differences are typically too large, although for some systems the experimental data exhibits large uncertainties. The only really "poor" numbers are HF/STO-3G and HF/3-21G results for acrolein, which show the high-energy *cis* conformer to be much more stable than it is known to be. Results for methyl- and *tert*-butylhexane and for 2-chlorotetrahydropyran are in good accord with the experimental data for all basis sets.

STO-3G and 3-21G[*] data for single-bond rotation barriers are compared to experiment in **Table 6-13**. All models are qualitatively successful in accounting for the observed barriers. Conspicuous failures include a very small *trans* barrier for H_2S_2 at the HF/STO-3G level, and an incorrect assignment of the conformation of H_2O_2 at the 3-21G level (*trans* planar instead of twisted).

Inversion barriers from Hartree-Fock calculations are compared with experimental values in **Table 6-14**. The smaller STO-3G and 3-21G[*] basis sets do not generally provide satisfactory results. STO-3G inversion barriers are typically much too large and barriers from HF/3-21G[*] calculations are typically much too small. Note in particular, that the nitrogens incorporated into both cyanamide and aniline are indicated to be planar.

The overall recommendation is that small-basis set Hartree-Fock models may be employed with some confidence for establishing conformational energy differences and rotation and inversion barriers. There are problem cases and, because of these, calibration studies are no doubt needed in advance of extensive applications.

6.5 Is it always necessary to utilize "exact" geometries to properly describe conformational energy differences and barriers to rotation and inversion, or will geometries obtained from lower-level calculations suffice?

As eluded to in the **Section 6.2**, determination of optimum conformation in flexible molecules is a computationally demanding task. Conformational energy differences are typically very small (a few kcal/mol), and high-level models may be required to provide accurate representations (see also **Section 6.3**). Conformational searching using sophisticated models will, however, often be prohibitively expensive and shortcuts need to be sought. One of these is to use equilibrium geometries from lower-level calculations, the hope being that bond length and angle changes accompanying conformational changes will be small, and that any errors due to the use of "approximate" geometries will in large part cancel. This being the case, both conformational energy differences and barriers to rotation and inversion obtained from high-level

Table 6-12: Conformational Energy Differences. Hartree-Fock Models

molecule	low energy/ high energy conformer	STO-3G	3-21G(*)	expt.
n-butane	*trans/gauche*	0.9	0.8	0.77
1-butene	*skew/cis*	0.8	0.8	0.2
1,3-butadiene	*trans/gauche*	1.8	3.5	1.7, >2, 2.5
acrolein	*trans/cis*	0.5	0.0	2.0, 2.06
glyoxal	*trans/cis*	1.5	5.1	3.2
methylcyclohexane	*equatorial/axial*	1.8	1.9	1.8
tert-butylcyclohexane	*equatorial/axial*	6.4	6.6	5.4
2-chlorotetrahydropyran	*axial/equatorial*	3.2	3.6	1.8

Table 6-13: Barriers to Rotation. Hartree-Fock Models.

molecule	STO-3G	3-21G[(*)]	expt.
BH_3-NH_3	2.1	1.9	3.1
BH_3-PH_3	1.0	1.7	2.5
CH_3-CH_3	2.9	2.7	2.9
CH_3-NH_2	2.8	2.0	2.0
CH_3-OH	2.0	1.5	1.1
CH_3-SiH_3	1.3	1.4	1.7
CH_3-PH_2	1.9	2.0	2.0
CH_3-SH	1.5	1.4	1.3
CH_3-CHO	1.1	1.1	1.2
HO-OH (*cis* barrier)	9.1	11.7	7.0
(*trans* barrier	0.1	0.0[a]	1.1
HS-SH (*cis* barrier)	6.1	8.8	6.8
(*trans* barrier)	2.9	6.2	6.8

a) HF/3-21G equilibrium structure for H_2O_2 is *trans*.

Table 6-14: Barriers to Inversion. Hartree-Fock Models.

molecule	STO-3G	3-21G(*)	expt.
cyanamide	3.3	0.0[a]	1.9, 2.0
aniline	2.7	0.0[a]	≈2
methylamine	10.5	2.3	4.8
ammonia	11.3	1.6	5.8
aziridine	27.3	13.0	>11.6, >12
phosphine	61.3	30.7	31.5

a) HF/3-21G equilibrium structures for cyanamide and aniline both incorporate planar nitrogen.

calculations, but based on geometries obtained from lower-level models (including semi-empirical models), should closely approximate those based on full (high level) geometry optimizations.

Such an hypothesis is easily tested. Examples of conformational energy differences for Hartree-Fock, density functional (SVWN and B3LYP) and correlated (MP2) level calculations, all using the 6-31G* basis set are provided in **Table 6-15.** In each case, three different geometries are examined, the first two being approximate geometries obtained from semi-empirical (AM1) and 3-21G(*) Hartree-Fock calculations, and the last corresponding to an "exact" geometry (HF/6-31G*, SVWN/6-31G*, B3LYP/6-31G* and MP2/6-31G*, respectively).

Overall, choice of geometry appears to have little effect on calculated conformational energy differences for all three levels of theory examined. Generally speaking, errors incurred from the use of approximate geometries are smaller than the differences between "exact" values and experiment. AM1 geometries are generally somewhat less suitable in this role than HF/3-21G(*) structures, but the differences are usually not great. Other semi-empirical and low-level *ab intio* models would be expected to lead ro similar conclusions.

Closely related is the question of the effect of choice of geometry on calculated rotation and inversion barriers. **Table 6-16** compares rotation barriers obtained from HF/6-31G*, SVWN/6-31G*, B3LYP/6-31G* and MP2/6-31G* calculations with experimental barriers as a function of geometry. As in the previous comparison, we examine the use of AM1 and HF/3-21G(*) geometries in addition to "exact" structures.

With one exception, 3-21G(*) geometries provide an excellent basis for rotation barrier calculations at all three levels of theory. The exception is hydrogen peroxide, where the 3-21G equilibrium structure is *trans* planar rather than twisted. AM1 geometries are generally not as successful; barriers are typically in error by a half a kcal/mol, and in one case (BH_3PH_3), by several kcal/mol. As with the description of conformational energy differences, some caution needs to be exercised.

Table 6-17 compares inversion barriers from amines and phosphines from HF/6-31G*, SVWN/6-31G*, B3LYP/6-31G* and MP2/6-31G* calculations, with experimental barriers, again as a function of underlying geometry. The differences noted here are somewhat greater than those previously observed for conformational energy or rotational barrier calculations. They may be traced to significant differences in the central angle about nitrogen or phosphorous obtained from the various levels of calculation. (For a discussion of the effect of geometry on electric dipole moments in nitrogen-containing compounds, see **Section 2.12**) The HF/3-21G(*) model, in particular, yields structures in which the local geometry about nitrogen is much closer to planarity than observed experimentally; this leads to inversion barriers which are too small. Use of AM1 geometries actually leads to much more satisfactory results.

The overall recommendation is to use approximate geometries from semi-empirical or low-level *ab initio* calculations (albeit with some caution), for evaluation both of conformational energy differences and barriers to rotation and inversion. Calibration studies in advance of applications may be desirable.

6.6 Do different methods produce different orderings of conformer stabilities?

The answer to this question is yes, but it is very difficult to quantify the answer. It is also very difficult to assess critically which models actually perform best in assigning the ordering of conformer stabilities. Aside from the identity of the ground-state conformer, there is typically very little known from experiment about complex conformationally-flexible systems. While there is too little experience with too few systems to draw broad generalizations, data at hand for acrylic organic molecules with two to four rotatable bonds suggest the following:

 i) *Ab initio* models with STO-3G, 3-21G$^{(*)}$ and 6-31G* basis sets usually (but not always) yield the same ground-state conformer. The semi-empirical AM1 model typically does not yield the same conformer.

 ii) The ordering of stabilities for low-energy conformers usually changes from HF/STO-3G to HF/3-21G$^{(*)}$ to HF/6-31G* models, although the changes are for the most part restricted to "switches" within this set of conformers and does not involve high-energy structures. The AM1 model does not provide similar sets of low-energy conformers.

 iii) The structures (dihedral angles) for individual low-energy conformers from the three *ab initio* models are quite similar.

6.7 Do conformational preferences change from the gas phase into solution?

The answer to this question is certainly yes. The extreme example is for proteins. These fold up tightly in aqueous solution, so as to maximize contact of hydrophilic regions with the solvent and at the same time to minimize contact of hydrophobic regions, but they uncoil (denature) in the gas (or in nonpolar solvents). The same fundamental driving forces must be present as well in smaller molecules, although the final effects are likely are likely to be much more subtle.

There is a lack of quantitative experimental data on this topic (no doubt there is good data on a few specific systems), and because of this we will restrict our comments to results from computation. Only experience will reveal the ability of the methods to accurately describe solvent effects and hence the validity of the conclusions drawn here. In view of the uncertainties involved, we consider only a single computational model, HF/6-31G* underlying (gas phase), and corrected for solvent using AM1$_{aq}$ (assuming HF/6-31G* geometries).

Gas and "aqueous phase" conformational energy differences are presented in **Table 6-18**. The effects are very small for hydrocarbons, but reach 1-2 kcal/mol where heteroatoms are involved. The largest effect is for 2-chloro-tetrahydropyran, where inclusion of solvent increases the preference for the *axial* conformer by nearly 2 kcal/mol.

Solvent effects on single-bond rotation barriers are exemplified by the data in **Table 6-19**. Again, the solvent generally exerts only a modest influence, the largest effects being to lower the *cis* barrier in hydrogen peroxide by 1.1 kcal/mol and to raise the *trans* barrier in hydrogen disulfide by 1.3 kcal/mol.

Table 6-15: Effect of Choice of Geometry on Conformational Energy

molecule	low energy/ high energy conformer	HF/6-31G*//			SVWN/6-31G*//		
		AM1	3-21G[(*)]	6-31G*	AM1	3-21G[(*)]	SVWN/ 6-31G*
n-butane	trans/gauche	1.4	1.0	0.9	0.9	0.3	0.4
1-butene	skew/cis	0.6	0.7	0.7	−0.6	−0.5	−0.8
1,3-butadiene	trans/gauche	4.2	3.1	3.0	3.8	3.8	3.6
acrolein	trans/cis	1.9	1.8	1.7	1.8	1.6	1.7
glyoxal	trans/cis	6.1	6.0	5.6	4.4	4.3	4.1
methylcyclohexane	equatorial/axial	3.0	2.3	2.3	1.9	1.7	1.6
tert-butylcyclohexane	equatorial/axial	7.9	6.2	6.3	6.1	6.0	4.6
2-chlorotetrahydropyran	axial/equatorial	1.9	2.6	2.5	3.8	4.3	4.6

Differences

B3LYP/6-31G*//			MP2/6-31G*//			
AM1	3-21G(*)	B3LYP/ 6-31G*	AM1	3-21G(*)	MP2/ 6-31G*	expt.
1.1	0.8	0.8	1.0	0.9	0.7	0.77
0.1	0.5	0.4	0.3	0.5	0.5	0.2
4.3	3.7	3.6	3.7	2.7	2.6	1.7, >2, 2.5
1.9	1.7	1.7	1.6	1.4	1.5	2.0, 2.06
4.3	4.4	4.2	4.3	4.4	4.3	3.2
2.6	2.0	2.1	2.3	1.8	1.9	1.8
7.0	6.0	5.3	—	—	—	5.4
2.5	3.3	3.7	2.5	2.9	2.8	1.8

Table 6-16: Effect of Choice of Geometry on Barriers to Rotation

molecule	HF/6-31G*//			SVWN/6-31G*//			B3LYP/6-31G*//			MP2/6-31G*//			expt.
	AM1	3-21G(*)	6-31G*	AM1	3-21G(*)	SVWN/6-31G*	AM1	3-21G(*)	B3LYP/6-31G*	AM1	3-21G(*)	MP2/6-31G*	
BH_3-NH_3	2.6	1.8	1.9	2.7	2.4	2.5	2.6	2.0	2.1	2.7	2.1	2.1	3.1
BH_3-PH_3	6.1	1.9	1.9	5.5	3.3	2.9	5.5	2.5	2.4	6.0	2.7	2.6	2.5
CH_3-CH_3	3.5	3.0	3.0	3.2	2.9	2.9	3.3	2.8	2.8	3.6	3.5	3.1	2.9
CH_3-NH_2	2.7	2.6	2.4	2.5	2.5	2.3	2.5	2.6	2.4	2.8	2.8	2.6	2.0
CH_3-OH	1.5	1.3	1.4	1.6	1.5	1.7	1.6	1.5	1.4	1.6	1.5	1.5	1.1
CH_3-SiH_3	1.8	1.4	1.4	1.7	1.5	1.5	1.7	1.4	1.4	1.9	1.5	1.5	1.7
CH_3-PH_2	2.9	2.0	2.0	2.8	2.0	2.0	2.8	1.9	1.9	2.9	2.1	2.1	2.0
CH_3-SH	1.7	1.4	1.4	1.5	1.4	1.4	1.5	1.3	1.3	1.7	1.5	1.5	1.3
CH_3-CHO	1.1	1.1	1.0	1.3	1.3	1.2	1.2	1.2	1.1	1.0	1.0	1.0	1.2
HO-OH (*cis* barrier)	8.8	8.5	9.2	9.6	8.6	9.6	9.1	8.1	8.9	9.4	8.7	9.4	7.0
(*trans* barrier)	0.1	0.0[a]	0.9	1.1	0.0[a]	0.9	0.8	0.0[a]	0.7	0.6	0.0[a]	0.6	1.1
HS-SH (*cis* barrier)	8.5	8.5	8.5	9.5	9.5	9.2	8.4	8.5	8.2	8.7	8.7	8.7	6.8
(*trans* barrier)	5.9	6.1	6.1	6.0	6.3	6.0	5.5	5.7	5.5	5.7	5.9	5.9	6.8

a) HF/3-21G equilibrium structure for H_2O_2 is *trans*.

Table 6-17: Effect of Choice of Geometry on Barriers to Inversion

Molecule	HF/6-31G*//			SVWN/6-31G*//			B3LYP/6-31G*//			MP2/6-31G*//			expt.
	AM1	3-21G(*)	6-31G*	AM1	3-21G(*)	SVWN/6-31G*	AM1	3-21G(*)	B3LYP/6-31G*	AM1	3-21G(*)	MP2/6-31G*	
cyanamide	0.9	0.0[a]	1.1	0.4	0.0[a]	0.4	1.1	0.0[a]	0.9	1.8	0.0[a]	1.6	1.9, 2.0
aniline	1.6	0.0[a]	1.6	0.8	0.0[a]	0.5	1.5	0.0[a]	1.2	2.2	0.0[a]	2.1	≈2
methylamine	6.4	5.3	6.0	5.6	4.2	—	6.4	5.1	—	7.0	5.6	6.6	4.8
ammonia	6.6	5.4	6.5	5.8	4.2	5.2	6.7	5.0	6.4	6.9	5.3	6.6	5.8
aziridine	19.2	18.8	19.4	15.6	14.8	15.0	17.7	17.5	17.7	20.1	20.0	20.2	>11.6, >12
phosphine	36.4	37.8	37.8	29.4	32.6	33.0	35.6	35.1	35.5	33.2	35.4	35.4	31.5

a) HF/3-21G equilibrium structures for cyanamide and aniline both incorporate planar nitrogen.

Table 6-18: Solvent Effects on Conformational Energy Differences. HF/6-31G* Level

molecule	low energy/ high energy conformer	gas	aqueous[a]	expt.
n-butane	*trans/gauche*	0.9	0.9	0.77
1-butene	*skew/cis*	0.7	0.7	0.2
1,3-butadiene	*trans/gauche*	3.0	3.0	1.7, ~2, 2.5
acrolein	*trans/cis*	1.7	2.1	2.0, 2.06
glyoxal	*trans/cis*	5.6	4.6	3.2
methylcyclohexane	*equatorial/axial*	2.3	2.3	1.8
tert-butylcyclohexane	*equatorial/axial*	6.3	6.4	5.4
2-chlorotetrahydropyran	*axial/equatorial*	2.5	4.3	1.8

a) Calculated by adding the difference between the $AM1_{aq}$ and AM1 conformer energy differences to the (gas phase) HF/6-31G* conformer energy difference. HF/6-31G* geometries used throughout.

Table 6-19: Solvent Effects on Barriers to Rotation.
HF/6-31G* Level

molecule	gas	aqueous[a]	expt.
CH_3-CH_3	3.0	3.0	2.9
CH_3-NH_2	2.4	2.3	2.0
CH_3-OH	1.4	1.3	1.1
CH_3-SH	1.4	1.4	1.3
CH_3-CHO	1.0	1.1	1.2
HO-OH (*cis* barrier)	9.2	8.1	7.0
(*trans* barrier)	0.9	1.1	1.1
HS-SH (*cis* barrier)	8.5	8.0	6.8
(*trans* barrier)	6.1	7.4	6.8

a) Calculated by adding the difference between the $AM1_{aq}$ and AM1 rotation barriers to the (gas phase) HF/6-31G* rotation barrier. HF/6-31G* geometries used throughout.

Finally, solvent effects on nitrogen inversion barriers are examined in **Table 6-20**. With the exception of ammonia, the solvent acts to lower the barrier, sometimes significantly so, e.g., by 2.5 kcal/mol in aziridine.

6.8 Do simple computational models reproduce the known conformational differences of reaction transition states?

Preferred conformation is an issue not only for stable molecules but also for transition states. The problems of knowing what conformer or conformers need to be considered and how exactly to go about identifying them are exactly the same, except for the added complication that we have no (direct) experimental data to guide us. Our treatment here is cursory and we provide only two very closely-related examples.

Experimentally, both Cope and Claisen rearrangements are known to proceed (wherever possible) via *chair-like* as opposed to *boat-like* transition states. The differences in activation energies are not precisely known for either parent system (1,5-hexadiene and vinyl,allyl ether), but are something on the order of 5.7 kcal/mol and 3.0 kcal/mol for Cope and Claisen rearrangements, respectively.

Calculated (AM1, HF/STO-3G, HF/3-21G and HF/6-31G*) *chair-boat* energy differences for Cope and Claisen rearrangements are given in **Table 6-21**. All levels of calculation (including AM1) correctly reproduce the experimental observation that *chair* transition states are favored over alternative *boat* structures for both Cope and Claisen rearrangements. Calculated *chair-boat* energy differences are consistently (and significantly) larger than what might be expected based on experimental activation energy differences for both reactions and for all levels of theory. For comparison, *chair-boat* energy differences in cyclohexane (3.5, 7.0, 7.6 and 7.8 kcal/mol for AM1, STO-3G, 3-21G and 6-31G* calculations, respectively) are (except for AM1) quite close to the experimental estimate (5-6 kcal/mol).

The apparent overestimation of *chair-boat* energy differences in both Cope and Claisen rearrangements (in contrast to the favorable performance of the theory for cyclohexane) is possibly not a flaw in the calculations but may in fact arise because rearrangments via *chair* and *boat* transition states do not initiate from the same ground state conformer (see also **Section 6.1**). Were this the case, the actual experimental data would not be interpreted in terms of a difference in energies between *chair* and *boat* transition states, but rather as a difference in activation energies starting from the appropriate reactant conformers.

6.9 What is the best way to represent and interpret potentials for rotation about single bonds?

Empirical force fields used in molecular mechanics/molecular dynamics calculations all share common components, among them components which describe bond stretching, angle bending and torsional motions, as well as components which account for non-bonded steric and electrostatic interactions. While most of the information needed to parameterize force fields can

Table 6-20: **Solvent Effects on Barriers to Inversion.**
HF/6-31G* Level

molecule	gas	aqueous[a]	expt.
cyanamide	1.1	0.2	1.9, 2.0
aniline	1.6	0.7	≈2
methylamine	6.0	4.8	4.8
ammonia	6.5	6.9	5.8
aziridine	19.4	16.9	>11.6, >12

a) Calculated by adding the difference between the $AM1_{aq}$ and AM1 rotation barriers to the (gas phase) HF/6-31G* rotation barrier. HF/6-31G* geometries used throughout.

Table 6-21: Chair-Boat Conformational Energy Differences in Cope and Claisen Transition States

reaction	AM1	STO-3G	3-21G	6-31G*	expt.
Cope (1,5 hexadiene)	10.7	15.6	10.4	9.3	~5.7
Claisen (allyl, vinyl ether)	6.8	11.2	5.6	4.6	~3.0

be obtained from experiment, quite frequently critical data are missing. Information about torsional potentials, in particular, is often very difficult to obtain from experiment, and here calculations can prove of great value.

The energy of rotation about a single bond is a periodic function of the torsion angle and is, therefore, appropriately described in terms of a truncated Fourier series, the simplest acceptable form of which is,

$$V_1(\phi) = \frac{1}{2} V_1 (1 - \cos\phi) + \frac{1}{2} V_2 (1 - \cos2\phi) + \frac{1}{2} V_3 (1 - \cos3\phi)$$

$$= V_1(\phi) + V_2(\phi) + V_3(\phi) .$$

Here, V_1 is termed the one-fold component (periodic in 360°), V_2 the two-fold component (periodic in 180°) and V_3 the three-fold component (periodic in 120°). Higher-order (V_4, V_5, etc.) terms are generally not needed for the description of torsional motion in organic molecules, but additional terms may be required to account for bond rotations in asymmetric environments. Higher-order components are usually needed to properly describe torsional motions in many inorganic and organometallic systems. For simplicity, they are not considered here.

One advantage of this type of representation of overall rotational motion is that the individual terms may be readily and simply interpreted. For example, the one-fold term (the difference between *cis* and *trans* conformers) in n-butane represents the crowding of methyl groups, i.e.,

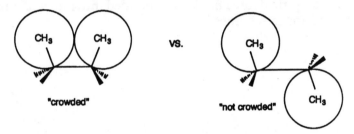

while the same term in 1,2-difluoroethane reflects differences in electrostatic interactions as represented by bond dipoles, i.e.,

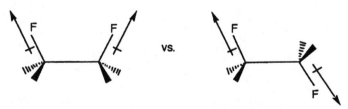

The three-fold component is perhaps the most familiar to chemists, as it represents the difference in energy between *eclipsed* and *staggered* arrangements about a single bond, for example, the difference in steric energies in n-butane.

The two-fold component is by far the most interesting term. It relates to the difference in energy between planar and perpendicular arrangements and often corresponds to the "turning on and off" of electronic interactions, as for example in benzyl cation.

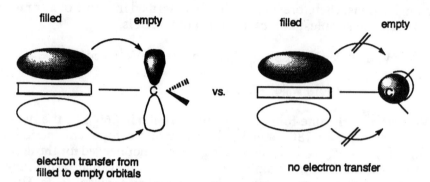

In this case, only in a planar arrangement may electrons be transferred from the filled π orbital on benzene to the empty orbital associated with the carbocation center. This leads to delocalization of the positive charge which contributes to the high stability of the planar cation.

The Fourier components, V_1, V_2, V_3, etc. may easily and uniquely be determined from calculated torsional energy curves. They provide not only an interpretive tool,[6] but also a compact and concise way of expressing torsional energy for use in empirical force fields incorporated into molecular mechanics and molecular dynamics schemes.

---

6. L. Radom, W.J. Hehre and J.A. Pople, J. Am. Chem. Soc., **94**, 2371 (1972).

7

Obtaining
Atomic Charges

Charges are part of the everyday language of organic chemistry, and aside from geometries and energies, charges are certainly the most common quantity demanded from electronic structure calculations. Charge distributions not only assist chemists in assessing overall molecular structure and stability, but also tell them about the "chemistry" which molecules can undergo. For example, the resonance structures for phenoxy anion,

indicate that the molecule's negative charge resides not only on oxygen, but also on the *ortho* and *para* (but not on the *meta*) ring carbons. This, in turn, suggests that addition of an electrophile will occur at these sites.

Despite their obvious utility, atomic charges are, however, not a measurable property, nor may they be determined uniquely from calculation. We explain why in **Section 7.1**, and then go on in **Section 7.2** to elaborate and compare two different procedures to arrive at charges from quantum chemical calculations. **Section 7.3** discusses the effects of electron correlation on atomic charges. Finally, in **Section 7.4**, we provide a "recipe" for calculation of atomic charges to be used in the construction of empirical potential energy functions for molecular mechanics/molecular dynamics schemes.

7.1 Why can't atomic charges be determined experimentally or calculated uniquely?

The reason that it is not possible either to measure atomic charges or to calculate them, at least not uniquely, is actually quite simple. From the point of view of quantum mechanics, a molecule is made up of nuclei, each of which bears a (positive) charge equal to its atomic number, and electrons, each of which bears a charge of –1. While it is reasonable to assume that the nuclei can be viewed as point charges, treatment of the electrons is more difficult. The simplest picture is that they form a distribution of negative charge which, while it extends throughout all space, is primarily concentrated in regions around the individual nuclei and in between nuclei which are close together, i.e., are bonded. The region of space occupied by a conventional space-filling (CPK) model, as defined by atomic van der Waals radii, encloses something on the order of 90–95% of the electrons in the entire distribution. That is to say, the space which molecules occupy in solids and liquids, corresponds to that required to contain 90–95% of the electron distribution.

How do we designate charges on individual atoms? We clearly need to account both for the nuclear charge and for the charge of any electrons *associated* with the particular atom. While the nuclear contribution to the total charge on an atom is easy to assign (it is simply the atomic number), it is not at all obvious how to partition the total electron distribution by atoms. To see that this cannot be done uniquely, consider the heteronuclear diatomic molecule, HF, sketched below.

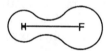

Here, the surrounding "line" is a particular "isodensity surface" (see **Chapter 8**), say that corresponding to a van der Waals surface enclosing a large fraction of the total electron density. The surface has been drawn to suggest that more electrons are associated with fluorine than with hydrogen, reflecting the known polarity of the molecule, i.e., $^{\delta+}H\text{–}F^{\delta-}$, as evidenced experimentally by the direction of its electric dipole moment. While this is qualitatively reasonable, how exactly do we divide this surface between the two nuclei? Put another way, are any of the divisions shown below better than the rest?

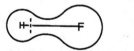
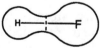
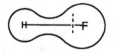

The answer to the first question is that it is not apparent how to divide the surface; the answer to the second question is clearly no! Atomic charge is not a molecular property, and it is not possible to provide a unique definition (or even a definition which will satisfy all). We can calculate (and measure using X-ray diffraction) molecular charge distributions, but we cannot uniquely partition them among the atomic centers.

7.2 What methods are available for calculating atomic charges and which are the most appropriate?

Two types of methods are now widely employed to assign atomic charges. The first is based on partitioning the electron distribution, while the second is based on fitting some property which depends on the electron distribution to a model which replaces this distribution by a set of atomic charges. There are many possible variations of each scheme; the criterion on which partitioning is based in the case of the former, and the selection of points and the property to be fit in the case of the latter. We discuss in turn a single variation of each type of scheme.

Partitioning Schemes

The electron density function $\rho(r)$ is defined such that $\rho(r)dr$ is the probability of finding an electron in a small volume element dr. It follows that,

$$\int \rho(r)dr = n,$$

where the integration is carried out over all space and n is the total number of electrons. In Hartree-Fock theory,

$$\rho(r) = \sum_{\mu}^{N} \sum_{v}^{N} P_{\mu v}\phi_{\mu}(r)\phi_{v}(r),$$

where $P_{\mu v}$ is an element of the density matrix, and the summations are carried out over all atom-centered basis functions, $\phi(r)$. This leads to,

$$\int \rho(r)\,dr = \sum_{\mu}^{N} \sum_{v}^{N} P_{\mu v} \int \phi_{\mu}(r)\phi_{v}(r)\,dr$$

$$= \sum_{\mu}^{N} \sum_{v}^{N} P_{\mu v}S_{\mu v} = n.$$

where $S_{\mu v}$ are elements of the overlap matrix. Similar types of expressions may be constructed for density functional and correlated models, as well as for semi-empirical methods. $S_{\mu v}$ in the latter is simply a δ function, i.e., 1 if $\mu = v$ and 0 if $\mu \neq v$. The important point is that it is possible to equate the total number of electrons in a molecule to a sum of products of density matrix and overlap matrix elements.

The question which remains is how to partition $\rho(r)$ among the individual products, and more importantly among the atoms in a molecule. Perhaps the simplest recipe is that proposed by Mulliken,[1] which as pointed out earlier must necessarily be arbitrary. In the Mulliken procedure, the above summation over pairs of atomic basis functions is divided into two parts: diagonal ($\mu=\nu$; $S_{\mu\nu}=1$) and off-diagonal ($\mu \neq \nu$).

$$\sum_{\mu}^{N} \sum_{\nu}^{N} P_{\mu\nu}S_{\mu\nu} = \sum_{\mu}^{N} P_{\mu\mu} + 2 \sum_{\mu < \nu}^{N} \sum P_{\mu\nu}S_{\mu\nu} = n$$

It is reasonable to assign any electrons associated with a particular diagonal element, $P_{\mu\mu}$, to that atom on which the basis function ϕ_{μ} is located. It is also reasonable to assign electrons associated with off-diagonal elements $P_{\mu\nu}$, where both ϕ_{μ} and ϕ_{ν} reside on the same atom, to that atom. However, how do we partition electrons from density matrix elements $P_{\mu\nu}$, where ϕ_{μ} and ϕ_{ν} reside on different atoms? Mulliken's answer was to give each of the two centers half of the total. Simple but completely arbitrary!

Within the Mulliken scheme, we can define a gross population, q_{μ}, for basis function ϕ_{μ},

$$q_{\mu} = P_{\mu\mu} + \sum_{\mu \neq \nu} P_{\mu\nu}S_{\mu\nu} .$$

Atomic populations, q_A, and atomic charges, Q_A, follow,

$$q_a = \sum_{\mu}^{onA} q_{\mu} \quad \text{and} \quad Q_A = Z_A - q_A ,$$

where Z_A is the atomic number of atom A.

As mentioned above, the Mulliken procedure for subdivision of the electron density is not unique, and numerous other recipes have been proposed.[2] Most of these make use of the overlap between atomic functions to partition the charge, and because of this, are identical to the Mulliken method for all current semi-empirical procedures (where atomic functions do not overlap).

Fitting Schemes

The idea here is to fit the value of some property which has been calculated based on the "exact" wavefunction with that obtained from representation of the electronic charge distribution in terms of a collection of atom-centered charges. Thus far, the only procedure of this type to receive serious attention is that based on the molecular electrostatic potential, ε_p.[3] This represents the energy of interaction of a unit positive charge at some point in space, p, with the nuclei and electrons of a molecule.

1. R.S. Mulliken, J. Chem. Phys., **23**, 1833, 1841, 2338, 2345 (1955).
2. (a) J.P. Foster and F. Weinhold, J. Am. Chem. Soc., **102**, 7211 (1980); (b) A.E. Reed and F. Weinhold, J. Chem. Phys., **78**, 4066 (1983); (c) A.E. Reed, R.B. Weinstock and F. Weinhold, *ibid.*, **83**, 735 (1985); (d) J.E. Carpenter and F. Weinhold, J. Mol. Struct. (Theochem.), **169**, 41 (1988).
3. (a) L.E. Chirlian and M.M. Francl, J. Computational Chem., **8**, 894 (1987); (b) C.M. Breneman and K.B. Wiberg, *ibid.*, **11**, 361 (1990).

$$\varepsilon_p = \sum_A^{nuclei} \frac{Z_A}{R_{AP}} - \sum_\mu^N \sum_\nu^N P_{\mu\nu} \int \frac{\phi_\mu(\mathbf{r})\phi_\nu(\mathbf{r})}{r_p} \, d\mathbf{r}$$

Here, Z_A are atomic numbers, $P_{\mu\nu}$ are elements of the density matrix and R_{Ap} and r_p are distances separating the point charges from the nuclei and electrons, respectively. The first summation is over atomic centers and the second pair of summations is over basis functions. Integration involves the coordinates of a single electron.

Operationally the scheme is carried out in a series of steps, following calculation of a density matrix P:

i) Define a grid of points surrounding the molecule. Typically this encloses an area outside the van der Waals volume and extending several Ångstroms beyond the van der Waals contact surface. It may comprise several thousand to several tens of thousands of points. The selection of a grid introduces arbitrariness into the calculation as the final fit charges depend on it. Note especially, that one has to be careful not to include too many "distant" points in the grid, as the electrostatic potential for a neutral molecule goes to zero at long distance.

ii) Calculate the electrostatic potential as defined above at each of the grid points.

iii) Determine by least squares, the best fit of all the points in the grid to an "approximate electrostatic potential" based on replacing the nuclear charges and electron distribution by a set of atom-centered charges, Q_A, subject to overall charge balance.

$$\varepsilon_p^{approx} = \sum_A^{nuclei} \frac{Q_A}{R_{AP}}$$

It is also possible to restrict the fit to reproduce the known (or calculated) electric dipole moment, although this is not commonly done.

Which method provides the better atomic charges? This we cannot answer. As seen in **Table 7-1**, each method offers distinct advantages and disadvantages, and the appropriate choice ultimately depends on what the charges are to be used for and to some extent on the available computational resources. *Ab initio* Hartree-Fock and semi-empirical charges for formaldehyde (**Table 7-2**) clearly show the extent to which the different methods lead to different results (sometimes greatly so), but offer no clue as to which are the most "suitable". Note, however, that while Mulliken charges obtained from Hartree-Fock models do not appear to converge smoothly with increasing size of basis set, charges obtained from fits to electrostatic potentials do appear to converge smoothly. This has been generally observed, and is considered a flaw in the Mulliken method; other partitioning schemes have been developed[2] specifically to overcome the problem.

Table 7-1: Advantages/Disadvantages of Common Charge Partitioning Schemes

scheme	advantages	disadvantages
Mulliken	computationally simple	does not converge with increasing size of basis set
fits to electrostatic potentials	converges with increasing size of basis set	computationally expensive

Table 7-2: Calculated Atomic Charges for Formaldehyde

	MNDO	AM1	PM3

Mulliken

H .00 / C +.29 =O -.29 / H

H +.07 / C +.14 =O -.28 / H

H +.01 / C +.30 =O -.31 / H

fits to electrostatic potentials

H -.11 / C +.71 =O -.48 / H

H -.05 / C +.53 =O -.44 / H

H -.10 / C +.68 =O -.48 / H

	STO-3G	3-21G	6-31G*	6-311G**

Mulliken

H +.06 / C +.07 =O -.19 / H

H +.14 / C +.21 =O -.50 / H

H +.14 / C +.14 =O -.42 / H

H +.09 / C +.20 =O -.38 / H

fits to electrostatic potentials

H -.03 / C +.35 =O -.29 / H

H -.01 / C +.48 =O -.46 / H

H +.01 / C +.44 =O -.46 / H

H +.02 / C +.42 =O +.46 / H

Convergence is not an issue in dealing with semi-empirical models. Note, that the MNDO and PM3 models give similar charge distributions for both Mulliken and electrostatic potential fit schemes, and that these depict a much more polar environment for formaldehyde than sugguested by the AM1 model. Note also, that AM1 charges for both schemes are quite similar to those obtained from the HF/6-31G* model. This does not necessarily mean that they are "better" than the corresponding MNDO and PM3 charges.

7.3 How does electron correlation affect atomic charges calculated at the Hartree-Fock level?

We have seen earlier (**Section 2-8**) that bond distances obtained from limiting Hartree-Fock models exhibit systematic differences from experimental lengths, and that these errors may easily be rationalized in terms of an operational definition of electron correlation. Here we extend that definition to account for changes in atomic charge distributions resulting from inclusion of correlation effects. We'll use a single example of formaldehyde, and then suggest the generality of the conclusion. Charges obtained from Hartree-Fock, SVWN and B3LYP density functional and MP2 correlated models all using the 6-31G* basis set from both the Mulliken partitioning method as well as on fits to calculated electrostatic potentials are given in **Table 7-3**. Note that charges resulting from the SVWN/6-31G*, B3LYP/6-31G* and MP2/6-31G* models which take explicit account of electron correlation are reduced over those from the corresponding HF/6-31G* model charge calculation schemes. The best way to interpret this is to recognize that electron promotion from filled to empty molecular orbitals (either implicit or explicit in all electron correlation models) takes electrons from "where they are" (negative regions) to "where they are not" (positive regions). In formaldehyde, the lowest-energy promotion is from a lone pair primarily localized on oxygen into a π^* orbital principally concentrated on carbon, i.e.,

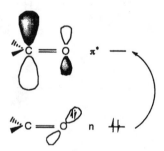

The basic conclusion, that electron correlation acts to reduce overall charge separation, is generally applicable. It is also supported by the observation that Hartree-Fock dipole moments are typically larger than experimental values, and that these are reduced by inclusion of correlation.[4]

Are changes obtained from correlated methods better than those from Hartree-Fock schemes? This we cannot answer, except to say that electron correlation leads to improvement in electric dipole moments (see **Section 2.12**),

4. J.E. Carpenter, M. P. McGrath and W. J. Hehre. J Am Chem. Soc., **111**, 6154 (1989).

Table 7-3: Calculated Hartree-Fock, SVWN and B3LYP Density Functional and MP2 Charges for Formaldehyde

	HF/ 6-31G*	SVWN/ 6-31G*	B3LYP/ 6-31G*	MP2/ 6-31G*

Mulliken

HF/6-31G*: H −.14, C +.14, O −.42
SVWN/6-31G*: H +.14, C +.00, O −.28
B3LYP/6-31G*: H +.12, C +.08, O −.32
MP2/6-31G*: H +.13, C +.06, O −.32

fits to electrostatic potentials

HF/6-31G*: H +.01, C +.44, O −.46
SVWN/6-31G*: H +.00, C +.37, O −.36
B3LYP/6-31G*: H −.01, C +.41, O −.39
MP2/6-31G*: H −.01, C +.41, O −.39

which are certainly related to charge distribution. Finally, it might be noted that it has been common practice to reduce charges obtained from Hartree-Fock calculations for use in molecular mechanics/molecular dynamics calculations. A brief discussion is provided in the next section.

7.4 What method is most suitable for obtaining atomic charges for use in constructing empirical energy functions for molecular mechanics/molecular dynamics calculations?

More and more, quantitative electronic structure calculations are called on to furnish parameters for use in empirical molecular mechanics/molecular dynamics schemes. This demand will continue and likely accelerate in the future, both as electronic structure models become evermore reliable, and as the empirical procedures are further extended into areas where experimental data are lacking.

The electrostatic energy, ε^{elect}, used in empirical force fields for molecular mechanics/molecular dynamics calculations is generally given by the following expression,

$$\varepsilon^{elect} = \sum_{A \, > \, B} \sum \frac{q_A q_B}{R_{AB}},$$

where q_A and q_B the charges on atoms A and B, respectively, and R_{AB} is the distance separating the two centers. The double summation is carried out over unique atom pairs A > B. Because it is an energy which we seek, the obvious procedure to obtain the atomic charges is by way of fits to calculated electrostatic potentials. Commonly, Hartree-Fock models have been employed with the 6-31G* basis set. The known effect of electron correlation in reducing overall charge separation as obtained from Hartree-Fock models (see **Section 7.3**) suggests that we might want to reduce the HF/6-31G* charges somewhat, or alternatively, utilize density functional or MP2 correlated models in place of Hartree-Fock models.

8

Graphical Models and Modeling Strategies

Computer generated graphical displays may serve not only to convey structural information, but also to provide insight into the results of quantum chemical calculations. Quantities which have proven of interest include the molecular orbitals, the total electron density, and (for open-shell systems) the spin density, as well as the electrostatic and polarization potentials. These are all functions in three dimensions $f(x,y,z)$, where x,y,z are Cartesian coordinates. One way to render them for presentation on a two-dimensional video screen[1] is to define a surface of constant value, or an **isovalue surface** or more simply, **isosurface**, i.e.,

$$f(x,y,z) = \text{constant}.$$

While the value of the constant is arbitrary, it may be chosen to reflect a particular physical observable of interest, e.g., the "electronic size" of a molecule in the case of display of total electron density.

Having defined an isosurface, it is possible to encode the value of some property as a function of a location on a particular isosurface onto the isosurface. For example, the value of the electrostatic potential (the energy of interaction of a point positive charge with the nuclei and electrons of a

---

1. Another common rendering technique is to define a two-dimensional plane or slice which cuts into the overall three-dimensional function, and to demark equal value lines (contours) onto this slice. *SPARTAN* provides both for isosurface and slice display.

molecule) may be encoded onto a total electron density isosurface representing the electronic size of the molecule, and be used to tell us something about the electrophilicity or nucleophilicity of particular regions of the molecule.

We first describe (**Section 8.1**) a number of quantities derived from quantum chemical calculations and which are well suited for graphical display. We then go on (**Section 8.2**) to suggest some broad modeling strategies, and finally, (**Section 8.3**) we recommend levels of calculation suitable for graphical models.

8.1 What quantities may be displayed graphically and how do they relate to molecular structure and reactivity?

Graphical representations of several quantities resulting from electronic structure calculations have already proven of value in modeling molecular structure and reactivity. These include molecular orbitals, total electron densities, spin densities in the case of open-shell systems and electrostatic and polarization potentials. We describe briefly each of these in turn, and in this and the next section suggest and illustrate their utility.

Molecular Orbitals

Chemists are very familiar with the π orbitals of ethylene, benzene and other planar molecules. They recognize that the nodal structure of the valence molecular orbital manifold provides a key to understanding why certain chemical reactions proceed easily whereas others do not. With some notable and important exceptions, e.g., the Woodward-Hoffmann rules,[2] such qualitative considerations have not, however, extended very greatly beyond planar π systems. In great part, this is due to the difficulty of constructing by hand and visualizing molecular orbitals of three-dimensional systems, a situation which modern computer graphics has now completely altered.

Molecular orbitals, $\psi_i(\mathbf{r})$, are written as linear combinations of nuclear-centered atomic orbitals, $\phi_\mu(\mathbf{r})$,

$$\psi_i(\mathbf{r}) = \sum_\mu c_{\mu i}\phi_\mu(\mathbf{r}),$$

where the $c_{\mu i}$ are the molecular orbital coefficients. As such, they are completely delocalized throughout the molecule, and may not be easily interpretable in terms of familiar chemical concepts, such as two-center bonds or non-bonded lone pairs. For example, inspection of the highest-occupied molecular orbital of sulfur tetrafluoride,

---

2. R.B. Woodward and R. Hoffmann, **The Conservation of Orbital Symmetry**, Verlag Chemie GmbH, Weinheim, 1970.

clearly reveals that it incorporates a lone pair on sulfur, in accord with its classical valence structure,[3]

but it also shows that it comprises significant contributions from other parts of the molecule.

Despite their obvious overall complexity, molecular orbital descriptions are often clearly related to "conventional" chemical indicators, and as such may be useful in interpreting chemical phenomena. For example, the lowest-unoccupied molecular orbitals (LUMO's) of planar (left) and perpendicular (right) benzyl cation,

clearly reveals the difference in charge delocalization of the two systems. Recall that it is into the LUMO, the energetically most accessible unfilled molecular orbital, that any further electrons will go. Hence, it may be thought of as demarking the location of positive charge in a molecule. The picture above reveals that the LUMO in planar benzyl cation is delocalized away from the cation center and onto the *ortho* and *para* ring carbons, in accord with classical resonance structures,

---

3. This is of course why the molecule adopts a trigonal bipyamidal as opposed to a tetrahedral equilibrium geometry.

while the LUMO in the perpendicular structure is almost entirely localized on the benzylic carbon. Our *chemical intuition* tells us that delocalization of the positive charge leads to energetic stabilization. Thus, planar benzyl cation is more stable than perpendicular benzyl cation.

A very similar, but less familiar, situation may be found for cyclopropyl-carbinyl cation. Examination of the LUMO in the lower-energy bisected structure (left) shows it to be delocalized throughout the molecule, in contrast to corresponding orbital in the higher energy perpendicular structure (right) which appears as more localized.

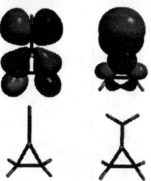

In this case, it is not easy to write classical valence structures (they are not as familiar as those for benzyl cation) and, therefore, not easy to deduce on this basis alone which structure is the more stable.

Total Electron Density

The total electron density, $\rho(\mathbf{r})$, for a (closed-shell) molecule is defined in terms of a sum of the squares of all occupied molecular orbitals. In the Hartree-Fock model, it is given by,

$$\rho(\mathbf{r}) = \sum_{\mu} \sum_{\nu} P_{\mu\nu}\phi_{\mu}(\mathbf{r})\phi_{\nu}(\mathbf{r}),$$

where the ϕ are atomic orbitals and $P_{\mu\nu}$ are elements of the one electron density matrix.[4] The total density isosurface (isodensity surface) demarks the locations of the electrons in a molecule. The quantity $\rho(\mathbf{r})d\mathbf{r}$ is the number of electrons inside a small volume element $d\mathbf{r}$ (see also **Section 7.2**), and is in fact what is what is measured in an X-ray diffraction experiment. Depending on the value of the isosurface, it may either serve to locate *chemical bonds*, or to indicate overall molecular size and shape. For example, a 0.1 electrons/au^3 surface of total electron density for cyclohexanone conveys very much the same information as a conventional skeletal structure model, that is, it depicts the locations of bonds,

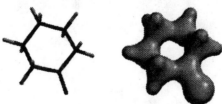

---

4. Other quantum chemical models yield qualitatively similar expressions for the total electron density.

while a 0.002 electrons/au^3 surface for the same molecule is much like a space-filling (CPK) model in that it depicts overall size and shape.[5]

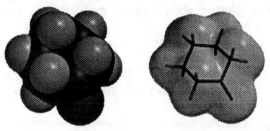

The obvious application of the former type of surface is to delineate bonding in situations where it might not be apparent. For example, the total electron density representation for diborane makes clear that the appropriate structural representation is one which lacks a boron-boron bond,

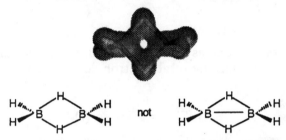

rather than one in which the two borons are directly bonded. The total density surface for cyclopropane seems to cast doubt on the idea that the σ bonds in highly-strained molecules are significantly displaced away from the line connecting carbon centers.

Perhaps the most interesting application of representations of this kind is to the description of transition states for chemical reactions. Here, one should be able to see clearly which bonds are being cleaved and which are being formed, e.g., in the pyrolysis of ethyl formate leading to ethylene and formic acid.

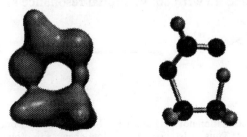

---

5. The radii used to define CPK models have been chosen to reflect the space which molecules take up when they pack in solids (or associate in liquids).

In this case, we see clear evidence of a "late transition state". The CO bond is nearly fully cleaved and the migrating hydrogen seems more tightly bound to oxygen (as in the product) than to carbon (as in the reactant). Further information, in particular about the timing of the overall reaction, may be obtained by replacing the static picture above by a "movie", i.e., animation along the reaction coordinate.[6]

Total electron density surfaces constructed to portray overall molecular size also have interesting applications. One of these might be to indicate relative ionic characters of molecules. For example, the images below clearly convey the impression that lithium acetylide (left) is less ionic than sodium acetylide (right).

Spin Density

The spin density is defined as the difference in total electron density formed by electrons of α spin and the total electron density formed by electrons of β spin,

$$\rho^{spin}(\mathbf{r}) = \rho^{\alpha}(\mathbf{r}) - \rho^{\beta}(\mathbf{r})$$

For closed-shell (electron-paired) molecules, the spin density is zero everywhere. For open-shell molecules, the spin density indicates the distribution of unpaired electrons. Spin density is an obvious indicator of reactivity for free radicals; bonds will be made to centers for which the spin is greatest. For example, the spin density in allyl radical,

suggests that reaction will occur at one of the terminal carbons and not at the center carbon, in accord with conventional resonance structures.

---

6. *SPARTAN* allows animation not only of the total electron density but any graphical object along a normal coordiante. Thus, it is possible to follow changes in orbital size and shape as well as charge distributions during the course of a reaction. See also **Section 3.5**. *SPARTAN* also allows construction and display of "blurred" pictures which conveys the impression of motion in a static image.

The same comment applies here as already made for molecular orbitals. While resonance structures are relatively easy to construct for simple systems and their interpretation relatively straightforward, there is much less experience in applying resonance arguments to larger (three-dimensional) systems. Additionally, resonance arguments are completely inadequate for discussions of subtle differences which are often critical in dictating structure, stability and reactivity, for example, differences caused by remote substituent effects or by changes in stereochemistry. In these situations, spin density distributions are able to provide a quantitative account.

For doublet states (free radicals) the distribution of spin (as defined above) is usually properly represented by the highest-occupied molecular orbital of a spin (neglecting the sign of the orbital). This simply reflects the ideal situation in which all electrons except that occupying the highest-energy molecular orbital of a spin are paired.

Electrostatic Potential

The electrostatic potential is defined as the energy of interaction of a point positive charge located at p with the nuclei and electrons of a molecule (see also **Section 7.2**).

$$\varepsilon_p = \sum_A^{nuclei} \frac{Z_A}{R_{Ap}} - \sum_\mu^N \sum_\nu^N P_{\mu\nu} \int \frac{\phi_\mu(\mathbf{r})\phi_\nu(\mathbf{r})}{r_p} \, d\mathbf{r}$$

The first summation is over nuclei A; Z_A are atomic numbers and R_{Ap} are distances between the nuclei and the point charge. The second summation is over atomic basis functions, ϕ_μ; $P_{\mu\nu}$ are elements of the one-electron density matrix, and the integrals reflect Coulombic interactions between the electrons and the point charge, where r_p is the distance separating the electron and the point charge.

Surfaces of constant molecular electrostatic potential map out areas which are both electron poor and electron rich. Positive isopotential surfaces indicate electron-poor regions where nucleophilic attack is likely, while negative isopotential surfaces indicate electron-rich regions where electrophilic attack is likely. For example, surfaces of constant negative electrostatic potential for trimethylamine, dimethyl ether and fluoromethane are an artifact of the non-bonded "lone pairs" of electrons.

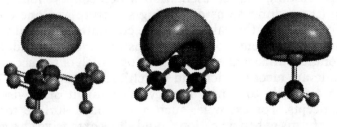

While the first of these results from a single non-bonded valence molecular orbital (the highest-occupied molecular orbital), the electrostatic potential in dimethylether and fluoromethane result from a combination of two and three high-lying molecular orbitals, respectively.

Polarization Potential

The polarization potential is the next term (beyond the electrostatic potential) in the expansion of the energy of interaction of a point positive charge located at p with the nuclei and electrons of a molecule.

$$\varepsilon_p' = \sum_i^{occ} \sum_a^{unocc} \frac{1}{\varepsilon_i - \varepsilon_a} \left[\sum_\mu \sum_\nu c_{\mu i} c_{\nu a} \int \frac{\phi_\mu(\mathbf{r})\phi_\nu(\mathbf{r})}{r_p} \, d\mathbf{r} \right]^2$$

The outside pair of summations are over all occupied and unoccupied molecular orbitals; ε_i and ε_a are orbital energies. The inner pair of summations are over atomic basis functions; the c are molecular orbital coefficients, and the integrals describe Coulombic interactions between the electrons and the point charge.

The polarization potential gives the energy of electronic reorganization of the molecule as a result of its interaction with a point positive charge. It is closely related to the molecular polarizability. This energy must be negative ($\varepsilon_a > \varepsilon_i$), and the sum of the electrostatic and polarization potentials must be a more negative quantity than the electrostatic potential itself. The sum of the two potentials provides a more realistic account of the energy of interaction of a point positive charge with the nuclei and electrons of a molecule than the electrostatic potential alone. For example, the electrostatic potential (at the heteroatom) does not reflect the ordering of gas-phase proton affinities of amines,

$$HF < H_2O < NH_3 ,$$

whereas, the sum of the electrostatic potential and the polarization potential correctly anticipates the experimental ordering.

Composite Surfaces

In general, isosurfaces may be encoded with the value of a property evaluated at the surface[7] leading to a representation which conveys four dimensions of information (three dimensions conveying structure and one conveying the property). For example, the value of the electrostatic potential may be color-encoded onto the total electron density isosurface (corresponding to the van der Waals contact surface), thereby, indicating which of the accessible regions on a molecule are electron rich and which are electron poor. This kind of imagery can also help to simply convey what might otherwise be difficult chemical concepts. For example, such an encoded surface for planar and perpendicular forms of benzyl cation would show extensive charge delocalization in the former but high buildup of positive charge centers in the latter.

---

7. Actually it is possible to encode simultaneously the values of two different properties on an isosurface, leading to a representation which conveys five dimensions of information (three dimensions conveying structure and two dimensions conveying two different properties).

8.2 What is the best way to use graphical models to describe molecular structure and chemical reactivity?

The total electron density for a molecule provides a quantitative measure of its size and shape. As previously commented (see **Section 8.1**), it can be employed in much the same manner as a conventional space-filling (CPK) model, which it closely resembles, e.g.,

to demark steric requirements, and (like space-filling models) thereby assist assignment of preferred products on the basis of sterics. Chemical reactivity and product selectivity, however, may depend not only on size and shape (whether reagent and substrate can approach each other and, if they can, what approach geometries are permissible), but also on electronic considerations. That is to say, reagent and substrate will be most likely to react when their individual electronic demands are complementary, e.g., a nucleophile with an electrophile. Electronic effects, which may or may not be completely independent of steric factors, also need to be properly taken into account in any realistic treatment of chemical reactivity and selectivity.

It is not yet obvious how best to gauge electronic preferences or, more importantly, to gauge relative preferences from one system to another. Relative sizes (extensions) of key molecular orbitals (the HOMO and LUMO) have been employed with some success, e.g., in the description of regioselectivity in Diels-Alder cycloadditions,[8] although it is now apparent that such treatments are limited in their ability to provide quantitative accounts of product distributions.

It is possible to quantify molecular orbital size and shape, and in particular to examine the asymmetry of key molecular orbitals relative to the total electron density. For example, simultaneous displays of the total electron density surface for an asymmetrical carbonyl compound such as cyclohexanone and the lowest unoccupied molecular orbital have been successfully interpreted as indicating not only where a nucleophile might best approach, i.e., where the LUMO is of greatest magnitude, but also where it would likely avoid, i.e., areas of high electron density.[9]

8. For a review, see: S.D. Kahn, C.F. Pau and W.J, Hehre, *J. Amer. Chem. Soc.*, **108**, 7381 (1986), and references therein.
9. S. Fielder, Ph.D. thesis, University of California, Irvine, 1993.

In this case the axial face (left) is the more accessible, in accord with the usual preference for nucleophilic attack.

An alternative indicator of chemical reactivity and product selectivity is the electrostatic potential. We have already suggested that this reflects overall charge distribution, and as such serves to delineate areas which are electron rich and hence subject to electrophilic attack, and those which are electron poor and hence subject to nucleophilic attack. Several examples, in which electrostatic potential is mapped onto an isodensity surface (demarking regions which are accessible to an approaching reagent) have already appeared in the literature.[8,10]

The development of models depicting product selectivity in organic reactions is still in its infancy. A number of existing schemes have already provided a qualitative rationale and several directions now seem to offer promise for a more quantitative account.

8.3 What levels of calculation are suitable for graphical models?

Even very simple levels of calculation, including small basis set Hartree-Fock methods and semi-empirical models, generally provide reasonable qualitative descriptions of molecular orbitals, total electron densities, spin densities and electrostatic and polarization potentials. On the other hand, description of subtle effects, for example, asymmetry of a particular molecular orbital, the total electron density, the spin density or the electrostatic or polarization potential due to remote structural differences, requires better methods. Semi-empirical models have proven to be unreliable for this purpose, as have Hartree-Fock schemes with minimal basis sets. This probably reflects the inherent inability of minimal basis sets to properly describe anisotropic molecular environments. Split-valence (and larger) basis sets in conjunction with Hartree-Fock models appear to provide a reliable account. There is too little experience to critique the performance of density functional and correlated models in this regard, although it would be expected that these would also provide adequate accounts.

10. Electrophilic additions: (a) S.D. Kahn, C.F. Pau and W.J. Hehre, J Am. Chem. Soc., **108**, 7396 (1986); (b) S.D. Kahn, C.F. Pau A.R. Chamberlin and W.J. Hehre, **ibid.**, **109**, 650 (1987); (c) S.D. Kahn and W.J. Hehre, **ibid.**, **109**, 666 (1987); (d) A.R. Chamberlin, R.L. Mulholland, Jr., S.D. Kahn and W.J. Hehre, **ibid.**, **109**, 672 (1987); (e) S.D. Kahn and W.J. Hehre, **ibid.**,108, 7399 (1986); (f) S.D. Kahn, K.D. Dobbs and W.J. Hehre, **ibid.**,110, 4602 (1988). Diels-Alder cycloadditions: ref 8a above and (g) S.D. Kahn and W.J. Hehre, Tetrahedron Lett., **27**, 6041 (1986); (h) S.D. Kahn and W.J. Hehre, J. Am. Chem., Soc. **109**, 663 (1987).

Appendix A
Performance and Cost of
Electronic Structure Models

Most important among many considerations involved in the selection of an appropriate quantum chemical model are the level of confidence required in the results and the computational resources available. Only rarely will it be possible to utilize the most sophisticated theoretical treatment available, and even then this may not be sufficient to guarantee the level of accuracy desired. Typically, practical concerns will dictate use of lower levels of calculation. Thus, it is important for the user to understand in some depth the capabilities and limitations of available theoretical models, from semi-empirical models which can be applied to molecules comprising more than a hundred atoms, to the simplest minimal basis set Hartree-Fock treatments, which may be applied to systems comprising up to one hundred atoms, to correlated models with large basis sets which are currently practical only for very simple molecules.

The present coverage is very brief and is limited to providing error statistics for geometry and relative energy calculations, together with very general comments. More detailed critique of the performance of the various theoretical models for structure and energies, as well as assessment of other important quantities such as conformational energy differences, vibrational frequencies and electric dipole moments, is available elsewhere.[1] Within our limited scope, data are provided for Hartree-Fock models, MP2 correlated models and SVWN and B3LYP density functional models, each with a variety

---

1. W.J, Hehre, L. Radom, P.v.R. Schleyer and J.A. Pople, **Ab Initio Molecular Orbital Theory**, Chapter 6, Wiley, New York, 1986; (b) W.J. Hehre, **Critical Assessment of Modern Electronic Structure Methods**, Wavefunction, Inc., Irvine, California, 1995.

of basis sets, ranging from minimal STO-3G (Hartree-Fock models only), to split-valence 3-21G$^{(*)}$, to 6-31G* and 6-311+G(2d,p) polarization basis sets. We have included the MNDO, AM1 and PM3 semi-empirical models.

Finally, we have provided some idea of the relative cost of application of the various models, both for single-energy calculation and for complete optimization of equilibrium geometry. The estimates which we have supplied are very rough, and depend not only on the specific case at hand, quality of the wavefunction guess and, in the case of geometry optimization, quality of the starting geometry and Hessian, but also on the program employed. Even so they may serve as a guide to method selection, at least to the extent as to help exclude models which are beyond the reach of available computational resources.

A.1 Errors in Equilibrium Geometries

Table A.1 summarizes errors in bond lengths connecting heavy (non hydrogen) atoms comprising first- and second-row elements only. The full comparisons between calculated and experimental equilibrium geometries from which these errors derive have been provided elsewhere.[1b] A number of generalizations may be drawn:

i) 3-21G$^{(*)}$ calculations using Hartree-Fock and SVWN and B3LYP density functional models all yield errors of comparable magnitude. Significantly larger errors are associated with calculations at the MP2/3-21G$^{(*)}$ correlated levels.

ii) Bond length errors for Hartree-Fock calculations do not change significantly in going from the 3-21G$^{(*)}$ basis set to the larger 6-31G* and 6-311+G(2d,p) representations. On the other hand, significant error reduction is noted for all correlated models (including density functional models) in going from 3-21G$^{(*)}$ to 6-21G*. The reason for this difference, already pointed out in **Chapter 2**, is that correlation involves the mixing of excited state electronic configurations the description of which requires basis functions of higher angular quantum number than needed for description of the ground state. Much less additional change in overall error is seen upon further extension of the basis set to 6-311+G(2d,p). At the "limit", the SVWN and B3LYP models present the smallest overall errors in bond lengths connecting heavy atoms. Sufficient data for MP2/6-311+G(2d,p) calculations is not available to draw meaningful comparisons.

What the statistics do not show is that Hartree-Fock and SVWN density functional bond lengths are nearly always shorter than experimental distances (the error is systematic), while bond distances obtained from B3LYP density functional and MP2 correlated models fall on both sides of experiment (the error is random).

iii) Bond length errors for HF/STO-3G calculations are generally somewhat larger than those for Hartree-Fock, density functional and MP2 calculations with larger basis sets.

iv) The PM3 semi-empirical model yields bond length errors which are significantly smaller than those from either MNDO or AM1 models. Recognizing that AM1 and PM3 are identical methods which differ

Table A-1: RMS Errors in Bond Distances in Two-Heavy Atom Hydrides

	STO-3G[a]	3-21G[(*)]	6-31G*	6-311+G (2d,p)
HF	0.055	0.032	0.032	0.035
SVWN	—	0.033	0.023	0.021
B3LYP	—	0.035	0.020	0.017
MP2	—	0.044	0.048	—
MNDO	0.048	—	—	—
AM1	0.048	—	—	—
PM3	0.037	—	—	—

only in parameterization, this points out the sensitivity of the performance of semi-empirical schemes on the method of parameterization.

Bond length errors for these same models for a series of molecules incorporating second-row elements with expanded valence octets ("hypervalent molecules") are presented in **Table A-2**. These results differ somewhat from those previously discussed for normal-valent compounds, and illustrate the danger of using error statistics alone to judge performance. The following comments apply:

i) The B3LYP density functional model and the MP2 model perform poorly relative to Hartree-Fock and SVWN density functional models for bond length calculations in hypervalent systems, irrespective of basis set. On the other hand, errors from both Hartree-Fock and SVWN density functional models are comparable to those found for normal valent compounds (see **Table A-1**).

ii) The HF/STO-3G model provides a very poor account of bond distances in hypervalent compounds. The reason is that d functions are required.

iii) Errors incurred by MNDO and AM1 semi-empirical schemes are also much larger than those encountered for bond distances in normal valent molecules. The PM3 model actually performs as well for hypervalent systems as it does for normal valent compounds, at least insofar as bond length errors are concerned.

Table A-3 summarizes errors in skeletal (involving heavy atoms only) bond angles. The following remarks may be made:

i) Hartree-Fock, density functional and MP2 models all provide very similar results for skeletal bond angles, irrespective of basis set. Errors in skeletal bond angles decrease in magnitude with increasing complexity of basis set for all models, although the reductions are not great.

ii) Errors in skeletal bond angles from the three semi-empirical schemes are 50% to 100% larger than those found for Hartree-Fock, density functional and MP2 models, depending on basis set. However, according to this measure alone, the semi-empirical models yield results which are quite acceptable for routine use.

A.2 Errors in Relative Energies

As already commented in **Section 4.1**, relative energy comparisons may be divided into categories depending on whether or not the total number of electron pairs is conserved, and if conserved, whether or not the numbers of each kind of electron pair are conserved. Our brief discussion here is divided along similar lines and considers individually errors in several different types of chemical reactions: (i) homolytic bond dissociation reactions, representing processes in which the total number of electron pairs is not conserved; (ii) hydrogenation reactions and energy comparisons among structural isomers, representing processes in which the total number of electron pairs is conserved

Table A-2: RMS Errors in Heavy-Atom Bond Lengths in Hypervalent Molecules

	STO-3G[a]	3-21G[(*)]	6-31G*	6-311+ G(2d,p)
HF	—	0.023	0.023	0.025
SVWN	—	0.030	0.030	0.025
B3LYP	—	0.037	0.037	0.037
MP2	—	—	0.036	
MNDO	0.093	—	—	—
AM1	0.099	—	—	—
PM3	0.034	—	—	—

a) minimal Slater type basis set for semi-empirical methods.

Table A-3: RMS Errors in Skeletal Bond Angles

	STO-3G[a]	3-21G[(*)]	6-31G*	6-311+ G(2d,p)
HF	1.7	1.7	1.4	1.3
SVWN	—	2.0	1.6	1.4
B3LYP	—	2.0	1.4	1.4
MP2	—	2.2	1.5	—
MNDO	4.3	—	—	—
AM1	3.3	—	—	—
PM3	3.9	—	—	—

a) minimal Slater type basis set for semi-empirical methods.

but the numbers of each kind of electron pairs are not conserved; and (iii) bond separation reactions and reactions comparing proton affinities among nitrogen bases, representing processes in which both the total number of electron pairs and the numbers of each kind of electron pair are conserved. No statistics are provided as there are too few data for meaningful quantitative comparisons. Rather, we limit ourselves to general comments.

i) Hartree-Fock models and local density functional (SVWN) models do not provide acceptable homolytic bond dissociation energies, irrespective of choice of basis set. All of the present generation semi-empirical schemes are also unsatisfactory in this regard. On the other hand, density functional methods (with the exception of the SVWN model) and the MP2 correlated model lead to reasonable homolytic bond dissociation energies. The 3-21G$^{(*)}$ split valence basis set is not satisfactory, but the 6-31G* and 6-311+G(2d,p) polarization basis sets lead to good overall results.

ii) Hartree-Fock models with 6-31G* or 6-311+G(2d,p) polarization basis sets give acceptable results for the energies of such reactions as hydrogenation, although the errors associated with HF/3-21G$^{(*)}$ calculations are probably of unacceptable magnitude. In the limit of very large basis sets, density functional and MP2 models provide a good account of hydrogenation energetics. However, smaller basis sets (including 6-31G*) are not as successful. None of the semi-empirical models properly accounts for the energetics of hydrogenation.

Similar conclusions apply for energy comparisons among structural isomers as for the hydrogenation energies above. Hartree-Fock, density functional and MP2 models perform reasonably well with large basis sets, but not as well with smaller representations. Semi-empirical methods provide a somewhat more satisfactory account here than they did for hydrogenation reactions, although the overall errors are still large enough to require considerable caution in applications.

iii) All levels of Hartree-Fock, density functional and MP2 theory properly describe the energetics of *isodesmic* reactions, including bond separation reactions and reactions relating acid and base strengths, and are all roughly comparable. Even small basis sets appear to provide overall satisfactory accounts. On the other hand, errors for semi-empirical methods are much larger.

A.3 Cost of Application

Aside from quality of results, the "cost of application" is the most important consideration in selection of a theoretical model. It is not straightforward to provide accurate estimates of the relative costs of various computational methods, for this depends not only on the method, but also on the problem at hand and on the availability of information with which to start a calculation, as well as on the specific program used to perform the calculations. However, rough guidelines can be set.

Before we proceed, we need to outline the different numerical procedures available for performing electronic structure calculations, in particular, *ab initio* Hartree-Fock and correlated calculations as well as density functional calculations, all of which require evaluation of large numbers of complicated integrals describing electron-electron interactions. The number of integrals formally increases as the fourth power of the number of basis functions, although many integrals are so small that they may be safely neglected. Still the total number of integrals which need to be handled can be substantial.

Because of the iterative nature of the problem,[2] the entire set of electron-electron interaction integrals needs to be accessed many times. It would seem then that the most efficient algorithm would involve first calculating and storing (on disk) all integrals, followed by as many accesses as required. While such a procedure is highly efficient both in terms of computer time and memory usage, it can be quite inefficient in terms of the real time. This is because disk access is very slow relative to processor and memory speeds. Such differences will likely further increase with developments in computer technology.

There are two alternative algorithms. The first involves storing integrals in memory as opposed to on disk. It is obviously very efficient (memory and processor speeds are comparable), but also obviously restricted in the size of systems which may be handled. 128 bytes of memory is sufficient only for closed-shell Hartree-Fock and density functional calculations on molecules containing about 100 basis functions. Open-shell calculations and MP2 correlated calculations require even greater storage. While memory sizes will continue to increase, it is unlikely that "in-memory" methods will provide a viable option for calculations on moderate to large organic molecules, let alone molecules of biochemical importance.

The second alternative is to forgo integral storage altogether, and simply recalculate integrals as required. Such a procedure, generally referred to as "direct", is not as inefficient as first impressions might suggest, and is rapidly becoming the method of choice for many applications. The main reason for this (aside from ever increasing arithmetic processing speeds) is that during the course of the calculation of the integrals are multiplied by successively smaller changes to the electron density, and more and more of these contributions can be quickly estimated and then discarded prior to actual calculation.

Direct methods which require no intermediate disk storage and very little memory, are really the only alternative for calculations on large molecules, i.e., those involving more than 300-400 basis functions. Here, use of disk storage would likely lead to unacceptable real time. Below 100 basis functions (depending on the amount of memory available) in-memory methods are an attractive alternative, and disk-based methods may be suitable in the range of 100-200 basis functions. No doubt, hybrid methods, utilizing whatever memory and/or disk is available, will develop.

Ab Initio Methods

As mentioned above, the computation time required for application of *ab initio* Hartree Fock models formally scales as the fourth power of the number of basis functions, η. This clearly represents an upper limit, and modern *ab initio* programs are able to eliminate very small integrals before

---

2. Reference 1a, Chapters 2 and 3.

they are actually calculated. An example of actual size dependence is provided in **Table A-4** for HF/6-31G* single-energy calculations on *trans* polyethylene as a function of chain length. Direct methods have been employed throughout. The timing data show that the power dependence is not η^4, but decreases rapidly with increasing molecule size and eventually drops below η^3.

A comparison of computational requirements for a single energy calculation on acetaldehyde as a function of basis set (this time using "in memory" methods) is provided in **Table A-5**. Here it is not sufficient to consider only the total number of basis functions to determine scaling, as the number of primitive Gaussians which make up the individual functions differ from basis set to basis set.

Finally some idea of relative computation times between in-memory and direct methods and between single-energy calculations and geometry optimizations can be gained from **Table A-6**. Here the comparisons are at the HF/6-31G* level for acetaldehyde. It is apparent that "in-memory" methods are significantly faster than direct methods, although the difference between the two decreases from single-energy calculations to geometry optimizations, reflecting the fact that the gradient evaluation step in both methods is the same.

Density Functional Methods

There are two fundamentally different approaches to density functional calculations. The first is closely based on Hartree-Fock theory in that it keeps the underlying core energy as well as the Coulomb energy, but replaces the Hartree-Fock exchange energy by a functional (a function of the total electron density and perhaps as well the gradient of the total density). In addition (and optionally), it adds another functional describing the correlation energy. This is the approach used in such programs as Gaussian 92/DFT[3] and Mulliken,[4] both of which can be accessed from *SPARTAN*.

Evaluation of the Hartree-Fock Coulomb energy goes as the fourth power of the number of basis functions. Numerical integrations involving the exchange and correlation functionals scale as the square of the number of basis functions times the number of integration points (which goes roughly in proportion to molecular size). For small numbers of basis functions, the latter step dominates, but rapidly becomes less significant. Density functional methods based on this approach cannot in practice be numerically superior to Hartree-Fock models (although they may produce better results).

The second approach to density functional theory involves treating the entire problem in terms of a numerical integration. This scales as the square of the number of basis functions times the number of integration points. Density functional calculations on very small systems will be slower than Hartree-Fock calculations, although the two methods will eventually cross in performance. In practice this crossover point is around 50–60 basis functions for the density functional module incorporated into *SPARTAN*.

The strictly numerical approach to density functional calculations is not applicable to "hybrid" methods such as B3LYP, which require the full Hartree-Fock Coulomb and exchange contributions.

---

3. Gaussian 92/DFT, Gaussian, Inc., Carnegie Office Park, Building 6, Pittsburgh, Pennsylvania 15106.
4. Mulliken, distributed by CAChe Scientific, P.O. Box 500, Beaverton, OR 97077.

Table A-4: Relative Computation Times for Acetaldehyde Using In-Memory Methods[a]

Basis Set	η	relative time
STO-3G	19	1
3-21G	35	3
6-31G*	53	19
6-31G**	65	36
6-311G**	78	78

a) obtained using *SPARTAN*.

Table A-5: Relative Computation Times for Direct HF/6-31G*. Calculations on trans Polyethylene, $CH_3(CH_2)_nCH_3$[a]

n	η	theoretical[b]	actual	x in η^x
0	42	1	1	—
2	80	13	10	3.60
4	118	62	31	3.30
6	156	190	62	3.15
8	194	455	105	3.05
10	232	931	160	2.98
14	308	2890	302	2.86
18	384	6990	500	2.81

a) obtained using SPARTAN.

b) $\eta4$ referenced to n=0.

Table A-6: **Relative Computation Times for 6-31G***
Calculations on Acetaldehyde[a]

task	method	relative time
single-point energy	in-memory	1
single-point energy	direct	5
geometry optimization (7 cycles)	in-memory	18
geometry optimization (7cycles)	direct	60

a) obtained using SPARTAN.

Semi-Empirical Methods

The computation time for application of semi-empirical models scales formally as the third power of the number of basis functions. This corresponds to the effort involved in matrix diagonalization. Integral evaluation steps in semi-empirical methods scale as the square of the number of basis functions.

Appendix B
Glossary

Following are brief definitions of a number of terms which commonly occur:

Ab Initio. "From the beginning". This is the general term used to describe methods seeking approximate solutions to the many-electron **Schrödinger Equation** which does not involve empirical parameters.

AM1. Austin Method 1. This is a semi-empirical method.

Antibonding Molecular Orbital. This is a **Molecular Orbital** which is antibonding between particular atomic centers. The opposite is a **Bonding Molecular Orbital**.

Atomic Orbital. This is a **Basis Function** centered on an atom. Atomic orbitals typically take on the form of the solutions to the hydrogen atom (s,p,d,f, . . . type orbitals).

B3LYP. Also known as **Becke3LYP** this is a parameterized hybrid Hartree-Fock/density functional scheme in which Becke's exchange functional is combined with the Hartree-Fock exchange and the Lee, Yang, Parr correlation functional is added.

Basis Function. These are functions usually centered on atoms (but not restricted as such), linear combinations of which make up the set of **Molecular Orbitals**.

Basis Set. The collection of atom-centered functions (**Basis Functions**) from which delocalized **Molecular Orbitals** are to be constructed.

Becke3LYP; see **B3LYP.**

BLYP. This is a density functional method in which Becke's exchange functional is combined with the Lee, Yang, Parr correlation functional.

Bonding Molecular Orbital. This is a **Molecular Orbital** which is bonding between particular atom centers. The opposite is an **Antibonding Molecular Orbital.**

Bond Separation Reaction. This is a special case of **Isodesmic Reaction** in which any molecule comprising three or more heavy (non hydrogen) atoms and described in terms of a conventional valence structure is broken down into the simplest (two-heavy-atom) molecules containing the same component bonds. The energies of bond separation reactions are well described using simple models.

Cartesian Coordinates. X, Y, Z spacial coordinates.

CID. Configuration Interaction Doubles. This is a limited **Configuration Interaction** scheme in which only double excitations from occupied to unoccupied molecular orbitals are considered.

CIS. Configuration Interactions Singles. This is a limited **Configuration Interaction** scheme in which only single excitations from occupied to unoccupied molecular orbitals are considered. This is perhaps the simplest method available to the description of excited states of molecules.

CISD. Configuration Interaction, Singles and Doubles. This is a limited **Configuration Interaction** scheme in which only single excitations and double excitations from occupied to unoccupied molecular orbitals are considered.

Configuration Interaction. This provides an account of electron correlation by way of explicit promotion (excitation) of electrons from occupied molecular orbitals into unoccupied molecular orbitals. Full configuration interaction (all possible promotions) is not a practical method and limited schemes, for example, **CIS, CID** and **CISD,** need to be employed.

Correlation Energy. This is the difference between the experimental energy and the **Hartree-Fock Energy,** or alternatively between the energy which would result from exact solution of the many electron **Schrödinger Equation** and the **Hartree-Fock Energy.**

Density; see **Electron Density.**

Density Functional Theory. This describes a class of methods in which exchange and correlation contributions have been formulated based on solution of the **Schrödinger Equation** for a free-electron gas.

Diffuse Functions. These are supplementary s- and/or p-type functions which extend far away from the nuclei on which they are centered. Basis sets incorporating diffuse functions are necessary for the description of the energetics of reactions involving anions.

Electron Density. This is a function which gives the number of electrons at a point in space. The function is defined over all space and summed over all space gives the total number of electrons.

Electrostatic Charges. This is a scheme whereby atomic charges are chosen to best match the electrostatic potential at points surrounding a molecule, subject to overall charge balance.

Electrostatic Potential. This is a function describing the energy of interaction of a point positive charge with the nuclei and fixed charge distribution of a molecule.

Empirical Force Fields; see **Molecular Mechanics.**

Equilibrium Geometry. This is the geometry corresponding to a minimum in the potential energy surface. It cannot actually be directly measured experimentally, for even at 0K molecules do not reside at the bottom of the potential energy well, but rather at a higher level (the **Zero Point Energy** level). In practice, equilibrium geometry can be inferred accurately from experimental measurements on different vibrational states.

Global Minimum. This is the lowest energy **Local Minimum** for a system of given stereochemistry.

Hartree-Fock Energy. This is the energy of system described in terms of the best single-determinant wavefunction.

Hartree-Fock Equations. This is the set of equations used to find the best **Single-Determinant Wavefunction.**

Hartree-Fock Wavefunction. This is the simplest quantum mechanically correct representation of the many-electron wavefunction in which the electrons are treated as independent particles. This is in terms of a sum of products in the form of a single determinant.

Hessian. This is the matrix of second derivatives of the energy with respect to the 3N-6 (N atoms) geometrical coordinates.

Heterolytic Bond Dissociation. This describes a process in which a bond is broken and a cation and anion result. The number of electron pairs is conserved but a non-bonding electron pair has been substituted for a bonding electron pair.

HOMO. Highest Occupied Molecular Orbital. This is the highest energy occupied molecular orbital.

Homolytic Bond Dissociation. This describes a process in which a bond is broken and two radicals result. The number of electron pairs is not conserved.

Hypervalent Molecule. This is a molecule containing one or more main-group elements in which the normal valence of eight electrons has been exceeded. Hypervalent molecules are common for second-row and heavier main-group elements but are uncommon for first-row elements.

Imaginary Frequency. This is a frequency which results from a negative force constant (in the diagonal form of the Hessian) which corresponds to an energy maximum.

Internal Coordinates. This is a set of bonds lengths, bond angles and dihedral angles (among other possible variables) describing molecular geometry. The **Z Matrix** is a special form involving only bond lengths, bond angles and restricted dihedral angles.

Intrinsic Reaction Coordinate. This is the name given to procedures with seek to "walk" in a smooth pathway connecting reactant and product.

Isodesmic Reactions. This is the name given to reactions in which the number of each type of formal chemical bond is maintained.

Isodensity Surface. This is a surface of constant total electron density defined by setting the value of the total electron density function to a constant.

Isopotential Surface. This is a surface of constant molecular electrostatic potential defined by setting the value of the molecular electrostatic potential to a constant.

Isosurface. This is a surface of a function in three dimensions defined by setting the value of the function to a constant.

Isovalue Surface; see **Isosurface**.

Kinetic Control. This refers to a chemical reaction which has not gone all the way to completion, and the ratio of products is not related to their thermochemical stabilities, but rather inversely to the heights of the energy barriers separating reactants to products.

Kohn-Sham Equations. This is the set of equations obtained by applying the **Local Density Approximation** to a general multi-electron system. A functional which depends on the electron density has replaced the Coulomb and exchange potentials used in the **Hartree-Fock Equations**. The Kohn-Sham equations become the **Roothaan-Hall Equations** if this functional is set equal to the Hartee-Fock Coulomb and exchange potentials.

LCAO Approximation. This approximates the unknown one-electron wavefunctions (**Molecular Orbitals**) in Hartree-Fock theory by linear combinations of atom-centered functions (**Atomic Orbitals**) and leads to the **Roothaan Hall Equations**.

Linear Synchronous Transit. This is the name given to procedures which estimate the geometries of transition states based on "averages" of the geometries of reactants and products, sometimes weighted by the overall thermodynamics of reaction.

Local Density Approximation. This is a simplification to **Density Functional Theory** in which the exchange correlation potential is restricted to being a function only of the local electron density.

Local Minimum. This is a **Stationary Point** for which all elements in the diagonal representation of the Hessian are positive. Chemically, a local minimum corresponds to an isomer.

Lone Pair. This is a **Non-Bonded Molecular Orbital**.

LUMO. Lowest Unoccupied Molecular Orbital. This is the lowest energy unfilled molecular orbital.

Minimal Basis Set. This is the smallest possible **Basis Set** needed to hold all the electrons on an atom and also maintain spherical symmetry.

Minimal Valence Basis Set. This is the smallest **Basis Set** needed to hold all the valence electrons on an atom and also maintain spherical symmetry. This is the basis set used in most present-generation semi-empirical methods.

MNDO. Modified Neglect of Differential Overlap. This is a semi-empirical method.

MNDO/d. Modified Neglect of Differential Overlap, **d** orbitals. This is an extension of the MNDO semi-empirical method which provides d type functions on heavy main-group elements.

Molecular Mechanics. This is the name given to empirical methods for structure and strain energy calculation based on simple bond stretching, angle bending and torsional expressions parameterized to fit experimental data.

Molecular Orbital. This is a function delocalized throughout the entire molecular skeleton which is made of contributions of **Basis Functions** at the individual atomic centers (**Atomic Orbitals**).

Møller-Plesset Perturbation Theory. This provides an account of electron correlation via implicit promotion of electrons from occupied molecular orbitals into unoccupied molecular orbitals, by way of a perturbation expansion of the energy.

MP2. This is **Møller-Plesset Perturbation Theory** terminated at second order. This is one of the simplest ways to introduce electron correlation. Higher orders of Møller-Plesset theory are referred to as MP3, MP4, ...

Mulliken Charge. This is a charge partitioning scheme whereby half of total number of electrons shared by a pair of basis functions is given to each basis function.

Multiplicity. This is the number of unpaired electrons (number of electrons with "down" spin) +1. 1=singlet; 2=doublet; 3=triplet; etc.

NDDO Approximation. This is the approximation underlying all present generation semiempirical methods. It says that two atomic orbitals on different atoms do not overlap (see each other).

Non-Bonded Molecular Orbital. This is molecular orbital which does not show any significant bonding or antibonding characteristics. A **Lone Pair** is a **Non-Bonded Molecular Orbital**.

Normal Coordinates. This is the set of coordinates which leads to a diagonal **Hessian**.

Normal Mode Analysis. This is the process of determining the set of coordinates (**Normal Coordinates**) which leads to the matrix of second derivatives of the energy with respect to changes in coordinates (the **Hessian**) being diagonal.

PM3. Parameterization Model 3. This is a semi-empirical method.

Polarization Basis Set. This is a **Basis Set** formed from an underlying **Minimal Basis Set** or more commonly **Split Valence Basis Set** by the addition of one or more sets of functions of higher angular quantum number than occupied in the ground state atom. This involves addition of p-type functions on hydrogen and d-type functions on main-group atoms.

Polarization Potential. This is a function describing the energy of electronic relaxation of a molecular charge distribution following interaction with a point positive charge.

Pople-Nesbet Equations. This is the set of equations describing the best unrestricted single determinant wavefunction within tha **LCAO Approximation**. These reduce to the **Roothaan-Hall Equations** for closed shell (paired electron) systems.

QSAR. Quantitative Structure Activity Relationships. This is the name given to attempts to relate measured or calculated properties to molecular structure.

Reaction Coordinate. This is the **Normal Coordinate** which corresponds to the negative element in the diagonal representation of **Hessian**, in that case where there is one and only one negative element. It connects reactant and product which are **Local Minima** on the potential energy surface.

Roothaan-Hall Equations. The set of equations describing the best **Single-Determinant wavefunction** within the **LCAO Approximation**.

SAM1. SemiEmpirical Ab Initio Method 1. This is a semi-empirical method.

Stationary Point. This is a point on the potential energy surface for which the gradient of the energy with respect to all 3N-6 (N atoms) geometrical coordinates is zero.

Semi Empirical. This is the general term used to describe methods seeking approximate solutions to the many electron **Schrödinger Equation** which involve empirical parameters.

Single-Determinant Wavefunction; see **Hartree Fock Wavefunction**.

Spin Density. This is a function which gives the difference in the number of electrons of "up" spin and "down" spin at a point in space. The function is defined over all space, and summed over all space give the difference in the total number of electrons of "up" spin and "down" spin.

Spin Multiplicity; see **Multiplicity**.

Split Valence Basis Set. This is a **Basis Set** formed from a **Minimal Basis Set** by splitting the valence region into two or more parts.

SVWN; see **Local Density Functional Models**.

Thermodynamic Control. This refers to a chemical reaction which has gone all the way to completion, and the ratio of different possible products is related to their thermochemical stabilities according to the Boltzmann equation.

Transition State Geometry. This is a geometry corresponding to a stationary point on the potential energy surface in which all but one of the elements in the diagonal representation of the **Hessian** are positive and one of the elements is negative. The transition state geometry is usually thought of as corresponding to the highest-energy point on a path connecting two local minima (reactant and product).

Transition Structure; see **Transition State Geometry**.

Variational. This describes a method for which the calculated energy represents an upper bound to the exact (experimental) energy. **Hartree-Fock** and **Configuration Interaction** methods are variational while **Møller-Plesset** methods, **Density Functional** methods and **Semi-Empirical** methods are not variational.

Vibrational Analysis; see **Normal Mode Analysis.**

VWN; see **Local Density Functional Models.**

Zero Point Energy. This is the energy of vibration at 0 K. This is equal to half the sum of the individual vibrational energies.

Z Matrix. This is a restricted set of internal coordinates (bond lengths, bond angles and dihedral angles only) describing molecular geometry.

Zwitterion. This is a neutral valence structure which incorporates both a formal positive charge and a formal negative charge.

236

Appendix C
Units

Geometry

Bond distances are given in Ångströms (Å) and bond angles and dihedral angles in degrees (°).

Reaction and Activation Energies and Heats of Formation

Reaction and activation energies are given in kcal/mol. Heats of formation are given in kcal/mol.

1 kJ/mol = 0.239 kcal/mol
1 hartree = 627.5 kcal/mol
1 eV = 23.06 kcal/mol

Dipole Moments and Charges

Dipole moments are given in debyes.
Atomic charges are given in electrons.

Vibrational Frequences

Vibrational frequencies are given in wavenumbers (cm^{-1}).

Index

In lieu of a "conventional index," we have provided a two-dimensional chart, one dimension enumerating molecular or chemical properties, and the other dimension referring to questions or issues raised in text regarding these properties. The order of the properties listed in the chart roughly follows the order presented in the text: equilibrium geometries, transition state geometries, thermochemical quantities, kinetic quantities, conformer energies and rotation/inversion barriers and electric dipole moments and atomic charges. The issues raised divide into categories roughly divided along the following lines: "how to... ", "effect of on... " and "performance of... ". Page numbers are provided within each relevant "cell" of the chart.

	discussion of	determination and verification of	semi-empirical vs. expt.	small basis set Hartree-Fock vs. expt.
Equilibrium Geometries	7, 72, 74	9, 19, 20	9	9
Transition State Geometries	85, 88, 90 102.124	85, 91, 95, 96	—	—
Bond Dissociation Energies	128	—	130	130
Hydrogenation Energies	128	—	130	130
Isomerization Energies	128	—	130	130
Isodesmic Reactions	129	—	130, 133	130, 133
Acid/Base Comparisons	129	—	131	131
Heats of Formation	131	131	—	133
Absolute Activation Energies	148	—	120, 148	148
Relative Activation Energies	148	—	120, 148	120, 148
Regio and Stereo Products	152	—	153	120, 153
Single-Bond Conformers	159, 160, 190	162	171	178
Rotation Barriers	190	—	171	178
Inversion Barriers	—	—	—	171
Electric Dipole Moments	—	—	—	23, 74
Atomic Charges	196	197, 204	—	—